Traditional Signalling

A Brief Design History

Michael A. Vanns

Ian Allan
PUBLISHING

Front cover:
Part of the LMR Standard lever frame in Bell Lane signalbox, Leicester. *Author*

Back cover:
Post-1893 GWR lower quadrant semaphores at Bewdley South, Severn Valley Railway. *Author*

Title page:
A pair of typical McKenzie & Holland bracket signals at York with crude finials. *Author's collection*

Left:
Westinghouse Brake & Saxby Signal Co A2 mechanical lever frame which developed out of Saxby & Farmer's last design patented in 1914 (No 4873) with tappet locking. Clearly visible is the angled locking tray with the tappets running through from top to bottom, connected to the catch-rod of each lever via the curved linkages. Running horizontally through the tray were the bars connecting individual locks which would engage or disengage with notches (ports) cut out of the tappet bars. Of the dozens of different types of interlocking, this was the one which stood the test of time. *Real Photos/Ian Allan Library*

Right:
Examples of the first standard upper quadrant semaphore adopted by the LMS, LNER and SR in the 1920s. The twin glass spectacle was a casting with the corrugated steel arm bolted on. This photograph was taken from the cab of No D262 at Leuchars Junction (ex-North British Railway) on 3 April 1965. *A. A. Vickers*

First published 2001

ISBN 0 7110 2811 7

Published by Ian Allan Publishing

an imprint of Ian Allan Publishing Ltd, Hersham, Surrey KT12 4RG.
Printed by Ian Allan Printing Ltd, Hersham, Surrey KT12 4RG.

Code: 0112/B1

Contents

Foreword

This book is an excursion around the huge variety of equipment that was developed to control the movement of trains throughout England, Scotland and Wales in the age of the steam-hauled train. The subject matter is considered predominantly from a design perspective, not a procedural one. It is a broad yet focused view, looking at signalboxes, signals and lever frames, electrical telegraph and block instruments. Inevitably, in a book of this sort, it is impossible to consider every aspect of signalling. There have to be limits and this author interprets 'traditional' signalling to be what was typical and representative of the period roughly extending from 1830 to 1960 when individual signalboxes controlled a layout that a signalman could see from his windows, and when the block telegraph provided the communication between signalboxes.

In many ways this work is a companion to my two previous general signalling books — *abc Signalling in the Age of Steam*, Ian Allan Publishing, 1995 and *An Illustrated History of Signalling*, Ian Allan Publishing, 1997. The former looked at the components of traditional signalling and put them into the context of procedures. *An Illustrated History* examined developments and the evolution of equipment in chronological order. This current work takes yet another view, focusing on each post-Grouping company in individual chapters and examining various aspects of the company's signalling and that of most of its constituent companies. (Some smaller pre-Grouping companies have had to be omitted due to lack of space.) The advantage of this approach is that it acts as a handy one-volume reference for enthusiasts, particularly when specialist company signalling histories do not exist. Where those detailed works are available, this book is a useful introduction to the subject. The disadvantage is the inevitable repetition of information because, contrary to what might be assumed, the signalling of pre- and post-Grouping companies had much in common.

The signalboxes, signalling equipment and procedures of every company seem, at first sight, to have been as individual and different as their locomotives and rolling stock. But very few pre-Grouping railway companies were completely self-sufficient when it came to designing, manufacturing and installing their own signalling hardware. Signalling contractors prospered during the Victorian era because they had so many British customers. Not only did they supply their own designs of signalboxes, lever frames, signals, point rodding, cranks, pulleys, level crossing gates, etc to railway companies, they also manufactured, and often installed, a range of products designed by their clients. In addition, they manufactured and installed equipment designed by rival signalling contractors if a particular railway wanted a 'standard' product. Stevens & Sons' tappet lever frame, for example, was manufactured at one time or another by Saxby & Farmer, McKenzie & Holland, The Railway Signal Co, Dutton & Co, Evans O'Donnell and Tyer & Co.

Once again I am grateful to all those signalling enthusiasts who have published their research, from which I have extracted most of the information for this work. It was also good to be given the opportunity by Ian Allan Publishing to produce a book with a selection of colour photographs. Unlike any other branch of railway operation, colour remains vitally important for the interpretation of signalling equipment. The colour of locomotive controls really made little difference to the work of footplate crews, but the difference between a red lever and a black one to a signalman was a matter of some importance.

Introduction

What characterised the Victorian era was mass-production achieved by division of labour and specialisation. Throughout the 19th century, processes were perfected that increased output without compromising quality. In fact, increased production almost invariably went hand in hand with an increase in quality or at least in consistency. Iron and steel production rose, and the new machine tools to work the resultant metal could turn out items more accurately than before. The rolling, cutting, bending, stamping and riveting of wrought iron and steel became more controllable. Better tools in the hands of an increasing number of skilled pattern-makers produced better wooden patterns for the production of more reliable and often sophisticated castings. Brick kilns could turn out hundreds of thousands of bricks of perfect shape, size and consistency, and wood-working machinery was developed that could reduce the largest hardwood into the finest instrument cabinet, or the tallest pine into the straightest signal post.

With mass-production came a reduction in the price of finished products. Quantity, quality and cost were all vital factors in the Victorian ethic, but so too was good design: what the Victorians might have defined as the art of turning a merely functional item into an elegant one. 'Fit for purpose' in the 19th century did not mean utilitarian. An object that was going to be visible invariably displayed some form of decoration or at least showed signs of having been designed to look pleasing.

Men such as John Ruskin and William Morris detested superimposed or inappropriate decoration on functional objects. They also believed mass-production had impoverished design and would lead to unforgiving uniformity. Morris despaired that men were being reduced to machines with no creative input into the work they were doing. Ruskin's and Morris's argument about decoration had validity, but this is where it is important to draw a distinction between the mass-production of basic materials and components, and the reworking of those materials and the assembly of components into more elaborate items. The parts of a mechanical lever frame may have been turned out in quantity, but the individual parts still needed hand-finishing or machining into shape so they could be fitted together with all the other components to create the finished product. In particular, the locking of each frame had to be tailored to the functions of the levers for a particular location and that was a skilled hand craft. Likewise, with hundreds of individual bricks, wooden joists to be cut to length, and tens of timber window sashes to be made and glazed, no two signalboxes were ever going to be exactly the same. That, too, depended on the skills of the bricklayers, carpenters, joiners, etc, and, of course, the location for the structure. The nearest signalboxes came to being mass-produced, and consequently standardised, were those created from individual prefabricated timber panels.

Consequently, despite Ruskin's and Morris's misgivings, the quality of engineering, the variety of finished products and the quality of workmanship achieved by the end of the Victorian era proves quite clearly that there was an enormous amount of pride and skill in the foundries and workshops of Britain. If variety can also be used as an indicator of creativity, then the hundreds of different patterns of lever frame by the beginning of the 20th century, when objectively one good design would have sufficed for the needs of every railway company in the country, prove that point. Not only that; the greater variety of products there was, the more employment opportunities increased.

The movement of trains on the very first railways was controlled by gesticulating policemen. Very soon these gestures were codified and a fairly standard Time Interval system of working trains was adopted by all railway companies. Once a minimum time had elapsed (varying from 15 to just five minutes) after the departure of a train from a station, another was allowed to follow it, having been given an appropriate caution signal by the station policeman. This cautionary period lasted another few minutes, after which time a driver could be given the all-clear to leave the station with no restriction. To signal these messages to drivers, policemen used various hand gestures during the day, sometimes reinforced by coloured flags, and coloured lamps at night — red for danger, green for caution and white for all-clear. These transitory signals were soon replaced by fixed signals — painted boards then semaphores — but the colours and their meanings were retained and in 1841 they were adopted as standard by all the country's railways.

During this period railway equipment was bespoke, invariably hand-made. Very little use was made of jigs, the quality of materials varied and castings were produced in small quantities only when they were needed. Basic blacksmithing, carpentry and bricklaying skills were sufficient to keep most railways running. (Locomotives, of course, were bought from contractors.) It was, nevertheless, a period of true inventiveness. Men like I. K. Brunel could and did challenge the prejudices of the day, championing atmospheric traction, the broad gauge, and the disc & crossbar signal. Before the supremacy of the semaphore signal was achieved in the following decades, fixed signals came in all shapes and sizes, and no two railways' equipment was alike.

In the 1850s, the production of signalling equipment became a more specialist trade, and there was enough demand for Stevens & Co (later Stevens & Sons), originally founded in the 1820s as a gas and general engineering firm, to concentrate on making and installing a range of simple mechanical signalling equipment for any company that could pay for it. During the 1860s the design of signalling equipment became a craze. Almost all the basic block instruments that were to serve the railways until the end of steam were developed in this period. At the time, however, they were largely untried, and this was also true for mechanical equipment. This decade was really one of theoretical innovation, when the ideas for mechanical and electrical railway gadgets on paper and in the Patent Office actually outnumbered those in use on the country's railways. Between 1866 and 1875 there were more patents for mechanical interlocking lever frames than at any other time in history, and yet only a fraction of those went into production, and fewer still stood up to the rigours of daily use. But the real historical significance of this period of fevered invention was that it heralded a change from empirical making to design and production. The man with the pencil and ruler was gaining supremacy over the man with the hammer and anvil.

What emerged from the 1860s were a number of firms with the ability to design, manufacture and install practical pieces of signalling equipment. Stevens & Sons, Saxby & Farmer and McKenzie & Holland soon became the main source of mechanical equipment, while E. Tyer & Co dominated the electrical signalling business. As far as publicity was concerned, Tyer eclipsed his rivals, but it must not be forgotten that there were many other firms since forgotten, for example Reid Brothers, London, which continued to supply main-line railway companies, including the London & North Western Railway (LNWR), Great Northern Railway (GNR) and North Eastern Railway (NER), with all their telegraph and block instruments.

The railways of the 1860s were still very crude affairs, but the period was a watershed between the days when signalling was a precarious art and a new period of comprehensive development. The upgrading of all aspects of railway operation really

Above:
A useful view of the back of the last British Railways standard upper quadrant semaphore. The twin glass spectacle was pressed steel with two grooves to accommodate the end of a corrugated steel arm. In this case, the later 1930s pattern enamelled flat-faced arm with turned edges was attached. Note the back-blind for obscuring the back-light of the signal lamp when the signal was pulled off. The cast-iron lamp cases were standard late LNER patterns. This photograph was taken at Clare on the ex-GER on 3 February 1967. *P. Hocquard*

started in the 1870s, a revolutionary decade when all the basic equipment, rules, regulations and procedures which were to serve the railways for over a hundred years were put in place. This decade witnessed the final rejection of the Time Interval system, and the realisation that separating trains travelling on the same line in the same direction by space not time was the only safe way of operating increasingly busy railways. The Block System — block working — provided that safeguard.

It was during the 1870s that a large number of the signalboxes which survived into living memory were erected. Many were highly decorated structures, but none was designed by architects. They were almost without exception the products of self-educated engineers. This in its own way illustrates how deep into society creativity extended. The only independent comment this author could find in the contemporary architectural press about the design of signalboxes was in *The Builder*, September 1876. In the lead article, entitled 'Railways and the Picturesque; Derbyshire', the editor, George Godwin, commented that railways had not been as destructive in the landscape as at first feared and, using the Midland Railway's (MR) line through Bakewell and Buxton as an example, he stated that the railway had actually increased the 'picturesque' nature of the area. At the end of the article he made a plea:

'Finally we would hint that something might be made of signal cabins, which, both from their outline and construction, as over-hanging chambers poised aloft on supports, and most frequently of timber construction, afford every suggestion for picturesque outline and character. They usually have the prevalent defect of railway structures, of looking much more weak and flimsy than they really are, and would be capable of being made far more pleasing objects without probably the slightest additional expenditure . . .'

Although published in 1876, Godwin was obviously referring to signalboxes of the 1860s, and it would be interesting to know what he thought of subsequent designs. Unfortunately, although a search was made through a further 20 years of *The Builder*, he remained silent as did his readers and fellow architects.

During the 1870s, demand for all types of signalling equipment increased, new signalling contractors sprang up and competition drove prices down. Contractors took the lead in developments, improving the quality of design and products to maintain an edge over their rivals. The three major firms producing mechanical equipment could all afford to employ more people, especially draughtsmen. It was no longer cost-effective to 'design' equipment on the work bench, for a blacksmith to make each part intuitively and for each signalbox to be designed afresh. Economy of production had to be achieved by having drawings and patterns of standard parts ready for the foundrymen and fabricators. There was a real need for standard but flexible signalbox designs. Contractors needed to be able to respond quickly to tenders, and efficient manufacturing and assembly capacity was vital to remain competitive. By the end of the decade many smaller signalling firms had not achieved this, and eventually disappeared (eg Easterbrook & Co, and E. S. Yardley & Co of Manchester).

What characterised the following decade was the containment of innovation. There was a dearth of new ideas. 'Variations on a theme' perhaps best describes the approach of railway companies and signalling contractors to their design work in the 1880s. Whereas in the 1830s and '40s there were dozens of completely different types of fixed signals, during this period one basic design — the semaphore — had completely supplanted every other form of fixed signal on main lines and yet was re-created in many different forms. The ergonomics of the lever frame did not change either, and all creativity was focused on trying to design a better type of locking. Although absolute block working was refined around three positive indications — Line Clear, Train on Line and Line Blocked — many railways were quite content to retain their two-position instruments. In the 1880s there was no Brunel to challenge the status quo.

At this time many more railways were prepared to go it alone with their own designs. Companies such as the MR, LNWR and Great Western Railway (GWR) had the manufacturing capacity and skilled workforce to become largely self-sufficient in the production and installation of both mechanical and electrical signalling equipment. The decade also witnessed the establishment of what was to become one of the most successful signalling businesses in the country — The Railway Signal Co. In 1881 George Edwards defected from the Gloucester Wagon Co taking with him his patents, a willing client (the Lancashire & Yorkshire Railway — L&Y) and all his accumulated knowledge from his days there and previously with Saxby & Farmer and the Signalling Department of the LNWR. The speed with which he started production also illustrates how by this time it was almost possible to set up any manufacturing business by mail order. Virtually all the machine tools could be purchased off the shelf, and there were numerous foundries that could offer a casting service if they were presented with the appropriate drawings. Dutton & Co (1888) and Evans O'Donnell (1894) entered the fray in this way with design drawings and patents to their names. The latter also had the advantage of acquiring an existing engineering works at Chippenham, Wiltshire.

With the passing of the 1889 Regulation of Railways Act, demand for signalling equipment again increased and competition once more pushed down prices. In 1872, Richard Johnson, the GNR's Engineer, was excited that Ransomes & Rapier was prepared to supply interlocking frames at £7 per lever. In 1893, Dutton & Co charged the GNR £3 2s per lever when it resignalled Holloway Carriage Sidings.

This was indeed a boom period for both new and replacement equipment. The years between 1890 and 1914 witnessed the erection of many of the signal posts, brackets and gantries that survived well into the 1960s. Most of the huge metal lattice brackets on the GNR, for example, dated from this period. By then, there was very little first-generation equipment left in use, and if there was, it had been heavily modified. Once interlocking and block working were completed, there was a slump in the market. Some traditional mechanical signalling contractors rediscovered the concept of innovation, McKenzie & Holland turning to the Westinghouse Brake Co in 1895 to market that firm's electro-pneumatic signalling systems, whilst others set up new businesses to jump on the power signalling bandwagon — J. O'Donnell of Evans O'Donnell formed the British Pneumatic Railway Signal Co Ltd in 1900. But, ultimately, salvation for all these firms came with amalgamation and by 1905 a new Consolidated Signal Co Ltd had absorbed all the assets of every independent firm with the exception of Stevens & Sons and Tyer & Co. In 1920 the Consolidated Signal Co Ltd became part of the Westinghouse group.

Between 1895 and 1920 the focus of the design process changed from the creation of functional but aesthetically pleasing mechanisms and buildings, to the quest for equipment and structures that were economical to make and operate no matter what they looked like. World War 1 also heralded a major shift in priorities, with a marked reduction in what was seen as unnecessary ornamentation on functional items. In some ways the 'art' went out of design. Engineers no longer needed an aesthetic sense. A piece of equipment was 'right' if it did the job it was designed to do. If it looked good as well, that was a bonus. Perhaps this exposed the dual standards of the Victorians, as truthfully much of the decoration of their machinery and the majority of their buildings was blatantly added on, superimposed like icing on a cake. The railway engineers of the 20th century believed the cake needed no icing.

Another feature of the post-World War 1 railway industry was the comparative anonymity of its designers. All signalling enthusiasts are familiar with the name John Saxby, but fewer will have heard about W. A. Pearce and his power interlocking frame (see p114). What few patents there were after the war were invariably registered to companies, not to individually named designers. The Peter brothers relay interlocking miniature lever frame (patent No 330637) is always referred to as the Westinghouse Style 'L' power frame. Perhaps this anonymity was an acknowledgment that 20th century design was a collaborative effort and not the result of one man's genius. World War 1 had made everyone suspicious of leaders.

With the Grouping of 1923 and the creation of four large railway companies (with a few smaller lines still remaining independent), came another upheaval in the railway industry. Absorbed company works were amalgamated and preferences had to be made in all areas of design. Rationalisation, however, never led to standardisation. In reality it would probably not have been cost-effective to try and achieve it, there still being useful capacity in existing workshops without the capital expense of retooling. There was so much Victorian equipment already in use that little change was obvious until the very end of the 1930s, but what was renewed between the wars was noticeably different to what had gone before.

There was also more use by all the 'Big Four' companies of the same new equipment, of which there was far less variety. For example, all but the GWR and Cheshire Lines Committee (CLC) adopted a standard upper quadrant signal design. This went through three stages of evolution very rapidly, but in essence remained the same basic design. The first manifestation had a cast-iron spectacle and a corrugated arm, the second a pressed steel spectacle and corrugated arm and the final variant the same pressed steel spectacle but an

Above left and above:
Moreton-in-Marsh signalbox photographed in May 1982 and then 28 years later from the same position. *C. J. Tuffs and Author*

enamelled steel arm with a flat face but turned edges at top and bottom to give it strength. All these variants found their way on to all parts of the London & North Eastern Railway (LNER), London, Midland & Scottish Railway (LMS) and Southern Railway (SR).

The number of lever frame designs available was drastically reduced as well, with only the GWR and LMS continuing development of their own in-house patterns. By 1924 Westinghouse Brake & Saxby Signal Co was marketing just one basic design, its A2/A3. Ironically, of course, what little new equipment there was, simply added to the huge range already in use. The 'Cheltenham Flyer', the 'Silver Jubilee' and the 'Coronation Scot' would all have encountered pre-Grouping lower quadrant oil-lit semaphores, upper quadrants and colour-light signals on their high-speed journeys to and from the capital. The SR was never able to replace all the block instruments it inherited with its own standard design, and C. V. Walker's double semaphore instruments of the 1860s (see page 107) remained stubbornly in use until the 1980s.

In the 1930s a certain flair returned to signalling. All the companies, with the exception perhaps of the LMS, let modern architecture influence their signalbox designs. Colour-light signalling continued to progress. The LNER and Westinghouse led the way in technological developments with route-setting panels. Bakelite became a legitimate substitute for wood. But another war precipitated entrenchment, and it was not until the late 1950s that fundamental change began to make serious inroads into the Victorian legacy. And at that point this author's story ends, before the rout. Today traditional signalling can been seen at its best only on preserved railways. What is left on the former British Rail network are pockets of mutilated equipment and buildings. At one time enthusiasts mourned the demolition of signalboxes, but when this author saw Moreton-in-Marsh signalbox had been fitted with PVC windows for the new millennium, he could not help feeling euthanasia might have been preferable to plastic surgery.

The order in which the pre-Grouping companies appear in the following chapters is dependent on the number of signalboxes each claimed to have in 1923, the company with the highest number appearing first.

1
The London, Midland & Scottish Railway

The two most important constituents of the new London, Midland & Scottish Railway (LMS) in England — the London & North Western (LNWR) and the Midland (MR) railways — both had very strong corporate identities by 1922. Stations, goods yard structures and engine sheds built in the late 19th and early 20th century were based on standard designs and were instantly recognisable as LNWR or MR. But there were hundreds of buildings still in use which exhibited a variety of architectural styles, buildings that had been erected early in the life of the LNWR and MR or by companies they had absorbed. Consequently, standardisation of design was strongest in the engineering departments that produced locomotives, rolling stock and signalling equipment, and it was the products of these departments which really distinguished one company from the other.

The L&Y also had a very strong identity, but as the company had been absorbed into the LNWR before the Grouping its influence on signalling matters by the time the new LMS was created had already been suppressed. In Scotland, both the Caledonian Railway (CR) and the Glasgow & South Western Railway (G&SWR) had their own signalling works, manufacturing and/or assembling mechanical equipment, and after the Grouping both these establishments continued to function. The only outward sign of a change of management north of the border was the gradual replacement of lower quadrant semaphore arms with LMS/LNER/SR standard upper quadrants on existing posts and other structures.

The frictions between ex-LNWR engineering staff at Crewe, ex-L&Y men at Horwich and ex-MR management at Derby hindered progress in LMS locomotive design until William Stanier was appointed Chief Mechanical Engineer in 1932, a new independent voice from the GWR. The same problem did not affect the new signal department to anything like the same extent. Old practices and loyalties at Crewe, Derby, Glasgow and Irvine did continue, but as there was little operational demand for immediate changes the frictions were not disruptive. When the LMS eventually created a new Signal & Telegraph Department in 1929, it was headed by A. F. Bound, a man with no allegiances to any LMS constituent company. Gaining a reputation for innovation on the Great Central Railway (GCR) and later the LNER, like Stanier he was an outsider who was able to command respect because of his undoubted mastery of his profession. The signalling part of Horwich Works had been disbanded before Bound's appointment, but in 1932 he closed the signalling works at Derby and concentrated all English manufacture and maintenance at Crewe.

Bound's reorganisations were quiet and pragmatic, and his individual mark on the new department was not as obvious as Stanier's on locomotive design. Changes were probably not as progressive as Bound might have wished, his experiments with 'speed signalling' using colour-light signals showing he was a man of vision. The systematic but gradual replacement of lower quadrant semaphore arms with upper quadrant examples and the erection of signals made from standard parts such as tubular steel masts during the 1930s sprang from solid engineering practice, but the work certainly did not evoke the same admiration as the exploits of the 'Coronation Scot'.

LONDON & NORTH WESTERN RAILWAY

1. Signals

The LNWR incorporated three pioneering lines: the Liverpool & Manchester Railway (L&MR), opened in 1830; the Grand Junction Railway (GJR), opened in 1837; and the London & Birmingham Railway (L&BR), opened in 1838. The L&MR was the first to use the Time Interval system of regulating the movement of trains between passenger stations in addition to the published timetable. By the 1840s this system was common on most railways.

The L&MR is credited with putting up the first fixed signal, a post with a lantern on top for use at night. It was not long before fixed signals were being developed for daytime use as well and the earliest of these consisted of a board that could be

Above:
The LNWR signal bracket which once protected the end of Platform 2 at Preston, photographed in the 1950s. Although the spectacles were the standard size, the corrugated steel arms were particularly short due to the restricted space. Because the distant arms were fixed, the LNWR lamps are clearly visible. Note also the calling-on arm, and the standard fabricated iron brackets. *W. S. Garth*

rotated. The first to be brought into use on the L&MR at Newton Junction at the end of the 1830s was capable of giving just two indications. When the red and white chequered side was turned to face approaching trains, drivers were being informed that another train was ahead of them. If the board was turned edge-on so that it could not been seen, this was to be taken as an indication that the line was clear.

The earliest representation of an L&MR fixed signal appeared in Wishaw's *The Railways of Great Britain & Ireland*, published in 1852. Illustrated alongside it was one of the first board signals used by the L&BR. This was shown as a flat circular disc with a white outer and a red inner ring mounted on a vertical spindle with a handle at the base to turn it through 90°. The GJR also used a disc signal rotating through 90° but, according to the illustrations provided for Richard Rapier's paper delivered to the Institution of Civil Engineers in 1873, the disc was in the shape of a semi-circle. After the LNWR was created in 1846 by the amalgamation of the three railway companies mentioned above, the new organisation began to erect signals with a circular disc mounted just above a rectangular board. These were copied from the disc & crossbar signals then in use on the GWR, and like those signals the rectangular boards had projections at each end. If the projections were beneath the crossbar this signified that the signal applied to down trains, and if the ends pointed upwards the signal applied to up trains. Unlike the GWR signals, however, the crossbar rotated with the disc, and there was no visible signal for the all-clear indication.

As the speed and frequency of trains increased, the LNWR, in line with other railway companies, progressively installed auxiliary signals to give drivers advanced warning of the indications of the fixed signals at stations. Then, during the 1850s and '60s, the disc & crossbar signals were gradually replaced by semaphores, those at stations being capable of showing three indications and those at junctions only two — danger and caution.

Many of those semaphores were purchased from Stevens & Sons, and after 1862 exclusively from Saxby & Farmer, which was employed to undertake all signalling work for the railway company. In 1873 the LNWR decided to appoint its first Signal Superintendent to create both a manufacturing and maintenance department at Crewe. Within a year the first standard semaphore had been designed and produced. It was essentially no different from the type of semaphore used by almost all other companies at this date: the arm pivoted in a slot at the top of the post and was worked by a rod attached to a counter-balance weight at the base. To give night-time indications, two designs of spectacles were manufactured, one with a single red glass, the other with a red and green glass. Both types of spectacle could be mounted either directly to the pivot of the arm or attached to the post a few feet below the arm. The twin glass spectacles were used on three-position signals, where the all-clear indication was displayed with the spectacle moved clear of the lamp, allowing its whitish light to become visible. Where the absolute block system was in operation and only two indications were

Left:
The final form of Fletcher's standard LNWR absolute block instrument. The case was tall enough to accommodate two needles and a larger indicator, which was attached to the knob of the commutator in permissive block instruments. In this photograph, the instruments nearest the camera were single-needle variants but elevated on the tubular brass legs substituted for the original cast-iron brackets from about 1903. *BR official photograph (1948)*

required, single glass spectacles with a red glass for the danger indication were used.

The next change in the design of LNWR semaphores came in 1883, when Crewe Signal Works began to produce a pattern that was to serve the company until it was absorbed into the LMS in 1923. The slot in the post was dispensed with and a new corrugated steel arm was made to bolt on to the end of a twin glass cast-iron spectacle acting as the counter-balance to return the arm to danger in the event of the drive rod or signal wire breaking. The LNWR was amongst the first to design such a semaphore, the current state of research suggesting that George Edwards of the Gloucester Wagon Co may well have been the very first — (see L&Y signalling on page 24). Although the absolute block system had by then rendered the caution indication redundant, most existing LNWR signals could still be worked to three positions. As the new semaphores were designed to display only two indications, the opportunity was taken officially to abandon three-position signalling and confirm that from then on the all-clear position was to be displayed with the arm lowered to approximately 45° — the old caution indication. For a number of years some LNWR semaphores displayed a green light as the all-clear indication, whilst others still showed a white. The latter was finally abandoned from 1893 onwards following the new Railway Clearing House recommendations of that year.

2. Signalling Equipment, Electrical

Throughout this book, various references will be made to Cooke & Wheatstone's electric telegraph. Of the partners, it was William Cooke who was the salesman, and in 1837 he persuaded the directors of the yet-to-be-opened L&BR to install a circuit with instruments to communicate between Euston station and Camden winding engine. Although Robert Stephenson, the railway's Engineer, was enthusiastic, the directors were less convinced of its usefulness and Cooke took his ideas instead to a more receptive GWR.

In the following decade the electric telegraph spread all over the country to become a commercially viable network for the transmission of public messages. It was used by railway companies to send general information between passenger stations, but soon it was recognised as a useful tool in controlling the passage of trains through tunnels, thereby reducing the risk of accidents. The next logical step was to extend its use to complete lines, an idea first advocated by Cooke in 1842, and by the early years of the 1850s this was very much on the minds, and consciences, of railway managers.

The SER (South Eastern Railway) was in the forefront of developments, but companies north of the Thames were less certain of the merits of what had by then been christened the Block System. At the beginning of 1854 the Electric Telegraph Co, which operated the country's telegraph network, persuaded the LNWR to adopt a form of block working. Approximately every two miles between London and Stafford signal stations were established where signalmen were put in charge of semaphores and two twin-needle telegraph instruments of standard Electric Telegraph Co design. If there were no trains between signal stations, the needles pointed to Line Clear, only being altered by the signalmen to Train on Line (originally Line Blocked) when a train was occupying that section of track. Once the train had passed through the section, the needles were returned to Line Clear. The Train on Line indication was sent by the signalman expecting the train, and Line Clear was re-established by the signalman who had just sent the train once he had been notified that it had passed out of the section. If there was a break in the circuit, the needle dropped to its vertical position, and this was soon adopted as the Line Blocked indication. Initially this new 'Two Mile Telegraph' was not operated on 'absolute block' principles and until the early 1870s LNWR signalmen at many places on the main line were still allowed to permit more than one train travelling in the same direction between signal stations, three-position signalling remaining in force with its caution indication.

The use by the LNWR of standard Cooke & Wheatstone twin-needle telegraph instruments also marked an evolutionary stage in their development. Originally the instruments had been designed to spell out messages by flicking the needles left and right. There had been no need to maintain the needles in either of those positions for any length of time. Because this was necessary for the new block system to work, the drop handles controlling the electrical circuit through the needles had to be wedged either to the left or right so that the needles could point permanently to either Line Clear or Train on Line. It is said that this was originally achieved with wooden wedges, but such a crude method was soon superseded by the expedient of drilling a hole through the shaft of the drop handles, allowing a steel peg to be inserted which rested on one side or the other of a triangular metal block. So that the pegs did not get mislaid, they were attached to the instrument by short lengths of brass chain — so giving birth to the peg-and-chain block instrument, destined to be used by many British railway companies throughout the 1870s and '80s.

When the LNWR made a serious attempt to extend the block system over most of its network in the 1870s, it put single needle peg-and-chain instruments into use as well as Tyer's one-wire system. Edward Tyer had made his reputation by designing momentary current block instruments which appealed to railway managers because the standard version with two needles, bell and plunger, required only one line wire (with an earth return) between signalboxes to create the necessary circuit. This compared with Cooke & Wheatstone/peg-and-chain-type instruments with a separate block bell which required three wires. As one of those cost-conscious railways, it was not long before the LNWR started to install Tyer's one-wire, two-position instruments for all new work, aiming, no doubt, to replace all its existing three-wire equipment. However, this was never achieved, and perversely even Tyer's own three-wire variants with separate pegging, non-pegging instruments and block bells were purchased and installed by the LNWR in this period.

In the 1870s the use of all the various types of instrument was not an operational problem because all the instruments were capable of displaying the required two indications — Line Clear and Train on Line. However, during the 1880s the rules of absolute block working were refined and the 'affirmative' system became the preferred option. This meant that Line Clear was only pegged on the instruments after the train had been 'offered' and an exchange of bell codes between signalmen had established that the line was actually clear. Until that had been done it was assumed that the line was blocked, or 'closed' to use the LNWR's preferred terminology. Train on Line remained in use to indicate that a train was in the section between signalboxes, but once it had passed clear, the needle of three-wire instruments was allowed to drop to its vertical position — Line Closed. On one-wire instruments it was not possible to give this third indication and, consequently, Train on Line had to double for Line Closed as well.

By the end of the decade the LNWR could no longer tolerate this compromise, so it was decided to adopt the three-wire, three-position system as standard. All existing instruments were to be replaced with a new design incorporating two needles, bell and taper in a single case. This saved space on the block shelves as only two instruments were then required in signalboxes controlling sections of double track. Although Tyer & Co already supplied such an instrument (minus the bell) to the LNWR, and would surely have been happy to modify that design to meet the requirements of such an important customer, the LNWR Telegraph Superintendent turned to his son, George Edward

Fletcher, to create a completely new three-wire block instrument for the company. The first attempt of 1888 was based very closely on the Tyer's twin-needle block instrument just referred to, and one wonders what that firm's reaction was to this development. By 1891 Fletcher's design had lost its sloping front, a characteristic inherited from the Tyer's design, and the upright rectangular wooden case had been elevated on two cast brackets so that the bell could be attached underneath. In 1892 a new Telegraph Works was opened at Stockport and a start was made on mass-producing the new standard instrument.

Once absolute block working had been adopted for all passenger-carrying through lines during the 1870s, the permissive system of allowing more than one train in a block section at a time was confined to large stations and lines dedicated to goods and minerals traffic. To give signalmen a permanent indication of the number of trains in a particular permissive block section, Edward Tyer developed a mechanism (which he patented in 1879 [No 1044]) attached to the commutator of his standard block instrument, in both one- and three-wire versions. When the first train was in the section, the mechanism (and needle) indicated Train on Line. When more than one train was in section, the needle remained at Train on Line but the mechanism displayed numbers from '2' upwards. This instrument, in both single- and double-needle form, was adopted by many railway companies, and the LNWR installed them at its larger stations in the 1880s. Eventually at the end of the following decade Fletcher adapted the mechanism so that it could be incorporated into his new standard block instrument. This required the height of the case to be increased slightly, and the new dimensions were then used for both absolute and permissive instruments.

So far we have only been considering instruments developed for use on double-track lines. For controlling the passage of trains over single lines, the LNWR was an early user of the train staff. By the 1870s the staff was augmented by the use of electric telegraph and paper tickets, the procedures being the same as those used on most other railway companies' single-track branches. Despite the usefulness of Edward Tyer's electric tablet system, patented in 1876 and progressively improved, the LNWR remained a firm advocate of the Train Staff & Ticket method of working. It was not until the very end of the 1880s that the company decided to improve on the system, and in order not to have to pay royalties to any independent contractor, F. W. Webb and the company's Signal Superintendent A. M. Thompson took out a patent in 1889 (No 1263) for an electric train staff instrument. Ironically, the LNWR did end up paying royalties on its instrument after Edward Tyer claimed it infringed his patents. £2 was paid for every Electric Train Staff instrument used on the LNWR.

3. Signalling Equipment, Mechanical

The story of LNWR mechanical signalling follows a similar path to that for electrical equipment. At first, equipment was purchased from contractors until the railway company became self-sufficient by manufacturing and maintaining its own.

In 1862 the LNWR signed an agreement with John Saxby to supply its signalling equipment to the company at fixed rates. This gave Saxby the incentive he needed to set up his own firm, and in May the following year he entered into a partnership with the Assistant Traffic Manager of the London, Brighton & South Coast Railway (LBSCR), John Farmer. The LNWR agreement was renewed in 1867, but it was not long before the railway company began to question its decision. During 1870 when John Saxby was petitioning for a prolongation of his 1856 'interlocking' patent, Stevens & Sons, the GWR, SER, LBSCR, LNWR, GNR and the relatively new signalling contractor McKenzie & Holland, joined forces to fight the case in the Privy Council. Despite successfully blocking Saxby's claim, the LNWR continued to patronise his firm until the end of 1872 when it finally decided to both manufacture and maintain equipment in-house.

The LNWR's Signal Department was created in 1873 and George Edwards (an ex-Saxby employee) was appointed superintendent in July that year. Manufacturing was concentrated at Crewe where Francis W. Webb was the Locomotive Engineer. Production did not begin in earnest until Edwards had left the LNWR in 1876 to join the Gloucester Wagon Co, and to understand the politics and the operation of the department during this period, Richard Foster's *A Pictorial Record of LNWR Signalling* (pp11-17), OPC, 1982, is recommended.

Francis Webb designed the LNWR's first lever frame and patented it in his name in 1874 (Nos 442 and 494). By then the company had had much experience with Saxby & Farmer interlocking frames and was keen to avoid any breaches of that firm's (or any other's) patents. Consequently, the Webb frame was a robust machine with a number of novel features. Compared with other designs, the catch-handles were not located immediately behind the tops of the levers, but were loops which protruded in front at about 45°. To release the catch, these loops had to be pushed down by the signalman before he could move the levers either forward of back. Frames were assembled from standard single-lever units incorporating all the necessary castings etc and quadrant plates which simply bolted together. Only the interlocking was tailor-made for each location.

Modifications and further patents followed in 1875 (No 462) and 1876 (No 2352), but the overall appearance of the LNWR lever frame had been established. The new 1876 'tumbler' design proved itself in use and with it the LNWR became truly independent of all mechanical signalling contractors. The final development came in 1901 when tappet locking was incorporated into an existing 'tumbler' frame. This form of locking had been developed by James Deakin of Stevens & Sons at the end of the 1860s and patented in the firm's name in 1870 (No 746). The patent had been allowed to lapse, but it was not until the beginning of the 20th century that

Right:
Part of the Webb Tumbler frame in the LNWR signalbox at Penybont photographed on 3 September 1963. Very obvious here are a number of plain quadrant plates where space was either left for future extra levers or where levers had been removed. When this photograph was taken, levers 6, 7 and 8 were already out of use, the drive rods to the locking beneath the floor having been disconnected, which explains why the loop handles on these levers were at a different angle from the others. *Andrew Muckley*

this simple and flexible form of interlocking was adopted by the majority of British railway companies, including the LNWR. The LNWR's first all-tappet locking frame was produced in 1903 but not patented.

Despite the considerable investment in the design and manufacture of mechanical signalling equipment, in the closing years of the 19th century, the LNWR, along with a few other British railway companies, took a radically new course in signalling design. The catalyst for this fundamental rethink was an increase in passenger and particularly freight traffic and the desire not to stifle this. By the 1890s the station and junctions at Crewe were at capacity and there were doubts that the proposed new layout could be efficiently controlled with existing mechanical equipment. In this decade, the Americans were turning to power systems in place of mechanical installations and the Westinghouse Brake Co had persuaded the British manufacturer and contractor, McKenzie & Holland, to market its new power signalling system. The Great Eastern Railway (GER), North Eastern Railway (NER) and L&Y took advantage of this arrangement, but in 1897, F. W. Webb and A. M. Thompson of the LNWR took out a patent for their own power signalling equipment.

A frame of miniature levers interlocked with miniaturised but mechanical tappet locking operated electrical switches which controlled the solenoid motors to work the signals and the magnet motors to change the points. Two basic types of miniature lever frames were designed: one with two rows of levers, the other with a single row. Although the power frames inside the new signalboxes at Crewe, Manchester London Road and Camden, where the Crewe all-electric system was installed, were radically different to existing LNWR equipment, the points and signals they controlled were of the company's standard design. Only the large vertical cylinders which housed the solenoid motors positioned beneath the semaphore arms, the large point motors and the rapid movement of the switch blades and the lack of point rodding and signal wires betrayed the presence of the all-electric system.

4. Signalbox Design

As on other railways, signalboxes as we would recognise them today did not appear on the LNWR until the late 1860s. Until then, a variety of ground-level huts and elevated platforms were used by policemen and later by signalmen to regulate train movements. From photographic evidence it appears that for the 'Two Mile Telegraph', two-storey brick buildings with wooden balconies were erected at various places. Although these buildings housed the telegraph instruments, they did not accommodate lever frames.

In the first few years of the 1860s, the Board of Trade's advocacy of interlocking pushed the LNWR into the arms of John Saxby, and signalboxes proper began to appear at various junctions, the earliest probably at Birmingham and Crewe. With the decision to apply the absolute block system to all its double-track passenger-carrying lines at the beginning of the following decade, Saxby & Farmer signalboxes, and their derivatives, were soon to be found all over the system. In addition, LNWR Divisional Engineers also erected signalbox structures of their own design. Most were small and built of brick with a hipped slate roof, obviously based on Saxby's design. Those on the Northern Division erected in the early 1870s have subsequently been classified as Type 1. Signalboxes with the same characteristics were also built at the same time along the Shrewsbury to Hereford line which the LNWR controlled jointly with the GWR. These signalboxes were unusually wide, which meant they were often square in plan.

In the same period on the Southern Division of the LNWR, a standard Saxby & Farmer signalbox design was adopted which has been classified as Type 2. These had top-lights above the operating room windows, a characteristic of Saxby boxes of this date. They also had hipped roofs, many being covered with zinc plates instead of slate tiles.

After 1874, the LNWR began to erect signalboxes of its own design. One particular feature was perpetuated as the design evolved and it continued to distinguish all LNWR signalboxes from those of other railway companies through to the Grouping of 1923. As in many early signalboxes, the operating room window sashes were only two panes deep, but to increase the amount of light entering the operating room, rather than add more glazing bars and panes of glass the LNWR simply increased the height of the panes. The ratio of height to width became more exaggerated as the box design changed over the years, and by the time the last manifestation of the LNWR's standard signalbox appeared in 1904, the ratio of height to width was 7:2.

The window sashes were not only a visible way of distinguishing LNWR signalboxes from those of other railways, but they were also used by the company to codify its structures. From 1874, the LNWR started to mass-produce window units, classifying the size of signalboxes by the number of units required. The first classification of the 1870s went from A to T, this being modified slightly in the 1890s by the addition of a new size of signalbox between R and S, the code being modified accordingly, running then from A to U.

The only other change between the first standard LNWR boxes of 1874 and those of later years was the abandonment of the hipped roof. Between 1874 and 1875 boxes remained predominantly small structures but, as they increased in size, gabled ends were preferred. Signalboxes with hipped roofs have subsequently been classified Type 3, with Type 4 used to designate those with the modified roof structure. The roofs of the latter type had no overhang at the gable end and only sufficient space on the front and back to accommodate guttering. From 1903 onwards, however, a more generous roof was provided, with a few inches added on the guttering edges and an aesthetically pleasing overhang at the gable ends. This became the Type 5 pattern, the last used by the LNWR.

Above:
Scout Green signalbox was built by the LNWR in 1871 when block working was introduced between Lancaster and Carlisle. It was a good example of the first generation of 'break-section' boxes, ie signalboxes not built at stations or junctions but on plain stretches of track simply to reduce the length of block sections between those places. *N. D. Griffiths*

MIDLAND RAILWAY

1. Signals

The earliest reference to a fixed signal on the MR appears in the mid 1840s, by which time the company was using the Time Interval system to regulate the movement of trains between stations. The signal consisted of a circular disc, painted red on one side and green on the other, fixed to the top of a mast with a lamp just below it. The mast could be turned through 180° so that the disc could be either face-on to approaching trains, to indicate either danger or caution, or edge-on, to indicate all-clear. Because the lamp was fixed to the mast, it had three lenses so that when it moved with the mast it could display a red, green or white light.

In October 1845 the company agreed to erect two semaphores at Derby and these may have been the first such signals on the MR. After this date they became the standard station signal, the lamps lit at night either by oil or gas, the MR being one of the first to experiment with the latter for signalling purposes. By the late 1840s the first references to wire signals appear in the company's minute books and as this terminology was used subsequently to describe auxiliary or distant signals, it must be assumed that from the end of the 1840s the MR was providing these signals to give advanced warning to drivers of the indications of station semaphores.

Above:
This overhead signalbox at Leominster was erected by the LNWR in 1901 during the period when it was responsible for signalling on the GW&LNWRJtR between Shrewsbury and Hereford. The superstructure was the standard Type 4 design, large enough to accommodate a Webb Tumbler frame of 80 levers. *R. E. G. Read*

Above:
Eastwoods Sidings signalbox was a good example of an LNWR Type 5 pattern, size 'E' structure. The nameboard on the front elevation was of the LMS's first standard type introduced at the end of the 1920s, but this particular box also sported two post-August 1935 nameboards fitted on either gable end.
V. R. Anderson

Progressively, semaphores were provided at stations and junctions with disc signals acting as distance or auxiliary signals.

The MR was never lavish or experimental with its signalling, but in 1857 it did install one of C. F. Whitworth's patent self-acting signals with an eye to future economies of operation. However, following the accident inside the LBSCR's Clayton Tunnel in 1861 (see page 100) the signal was discredited and the MR returned to more conventional signalling equipment aiming to standardise as much as possible. From at least 1853 it had already started to remove the GWR design of disc & crossbar signals it inherited with the acquisition of the Bristol & Gloucester line, replacing them with its own design of station semaphore and wire disc signals.

The first photographs of the earliest design of MR station semaphore signals (with arms for both up and down trains) show a square-sectioned timber post with a short pyramidical top (probably not a separate finial) and a slot for the wooden arms. The lamps were mounted on the front of the post at the bottom of the slot. At this period some MR signals used movable spectacles with coloured glasses in front of the lamps to alter the night-time indications, whilst others used lamps with different coloured glasses. Some photographs seem to show fixed lamp cases which would imply that it was the glasses that rotated inside. This arrangement had been patented by W. V. Greenwood and John Saxby in 1854 (Nos 683 and 1830) and the MR may have used this design of lamp. Other photographs seem to show revolving lamps. What is certain is that on single-arm signals the lamp was positioned on a bracket fitted to the right of the post at the bottom of the

Above:
An 1875 photograph of Mansfield Woodhouse signalbox taken shortly after the opening of the MR's new line from Mansfield to Worksop. The semaphore was an example of the first standard slot-in-the-post design used by the company until the 1880s. The signalbox was also a standard produce of the time, a Type 1 with operating room windows of the same size on front and end elevations.
Local Studies Library, Nottingham

Above:
A useful rear view of a standard post-1893 MR semaphore. Only the lamps were not MR patterns.
Ian Allan Library

slot. As three-position signalling was progressively abandoned with the perfection of the block system in the 1870s, both the arms and lamps were arranged to display only two indications.

In 1872 the MR established its own signal works on the banks of the River Derwent just outside Derby and soon became self-sufficient in the manufacture and repair of its mechanical signalling equipment. Semaphores began to replace board distant signals and, in line with Board of Trade requirements, from the mid-1870s they were distinguished from stop signals (home and starting) by the V-shaped section cut from the end of the arms.

This design of MR semaphore remained the standard until the end of the 1880s, by which time a new semaphore arm with integral cast spectacle pivoted on the front face of the post had been brought into use. It is obvious that the drawing office at Derby had set out to design a signal that was not only functional but looked good as well. Not only were the mechanisms carefully thought out, but so too was the positioning of the arm on the post and the adoption of a well-proportioned turned wooden finial in place of the utilitarian pointed cap used until then. As the simple cap had sufficed for so long, the new spike finial was certainly fitted more for aesthetic than purely functional reasons.

There is evidence that before the MR was made to adopt green as the all-clear night-time indication after 1893, the original spectacle incorporated only one circular coloured glass — red for danger. A number of these semaphores survived into the 1960s used as fixed distant signals. The two-position MR semaphore which appears in the majority of railway photographs, however, is the one with a twin glass spectacle casting designed to accommodate two circular coloured glasses. Needless to say, this spectacle casting had a number of subtle variants, photographs showing, for example, that there were some with different sizes of glass.

The final changes in MR semaphore design came shortly before and after World War 1, when painted corrugated steel arms began to be used instead of timber examples, and a few reinforced concrete posts were erected to replace timber ones.

2. Signalling Equipment, Electrical

The earliest direct reference to the use of the electric telegraph for the signalling of trains on the MR is found in Board Meeting minutes of November 1844. At that meeting it was recommended that the telegraph be brought into use through Clay Cross Tunnel. After this the MR was no more or less advanced than any other railway company north of the Thames in using the telegraph for controlling train movements. As the Board of Trade began to advocate more strongly the adoption of block signalling in the following two decades, its use gradually spread over the MR.

The instruments the MR chose for block working were standard single-needle examples, with signalling codes exchanged between signalboxes on single-stroke bells. The evidence suggests that the standard indicating instruments, both pegging and non-pegging, were manufactured for the company by the same specialist independent instrument makers who supplied the NER, GNR, CLC, CR and North British Railway (NBR). The standard design was modified for each company in very minor ways. For example, the MR favoured a plain green background to the single needle which was painted black, the three indications of Line Clear, Line Blocked and Train on Line being painted on to the zinc plate which surrounded the needle movement.

Until the 1880s, the familiar steel peg attached by a brass chain was used to secure the position of the drop handle on pegging instruments. To supersede this arrangement so that the signalman could peg an indication using just one hand, W. E. Langdon, the company's Superintendent and Engineer of the Electrical Department, patented in 1884 (No 61) a catch which was positioned underneath the drop handle shaft and could be manipulated with the forefinger. As with all other railway companies, MR non-pegging instruments also had a drop handle which, although it could not be pegged permanently in position, was used to exchange dial signals between signalboxes in the same way as on speaking telegraph instruments. When the Railway Clearing House standard block signalling regulations of 1895 no longer required the use of dial signals to reinforce bell codes, the MR used the drop handles of its non-pegging instruments to transmit routeing codes.

MR block bells were derived from the 1860s designs of C. V. Walker and W. H. Preece with the bell mounted above the wooden case containing the electro-magnets. As was common practice when using such instruments, the MR had a variety of sizes and shapes of brass bell so that the signalman could identify which bell had sounded by the different tones. The MR also went one step further and in larger signalboxes with a number of block bells, the instruments were fitted with a small metal disc which, when the bell was struck, dropped out of a vertical slot in the case adjacent to the tapper,

Above:
A June 1960 photograph of a MR gantry at Trent, Nottingham. Note the single glass cast-iron spectacles on the fixed (non-operational) distant arms. This spectacle design may have been the first to be fitted to arms in the late 1880s and early 1890s, before the Railway Clearing House recommendations of 1893 requiring all companies to adopt a green all-clear light instead of white. Notice also that the post-1893 twin glass spectacles on the home signals were not all of the same pattern.
D. Ibbotson

giving the signalmen a visual reminder as to which bell had sounded. The discs had to be pushed back into the case to 'reset' the instrument and were probably prone to being bent which might explain why the use of the device did not survive into LMS days. Another unique feature of MR bells, which was also abandoned by the LMS, was the use of a generously sized tapper which resembled the seat of a miniature easy chair.

The MR was for many years very conservative in its use of block instruments, never using train describers, special permissive instruments or Sykes 'Lock & Block'. Nevertheless, W. E. Langdon had long appreciated the benefits of linking the operation of the fixed signals and block instruments with some means of train detection. Before joining the MR he had been Superintendent of Telegraphs on the LSWR, taking out a patent in 1870 (No 1268) jointly with W. H. Preece for an electrical link between block instrument and fixed signal. When Langdon was given the opportunity to experiment on the MR, he was keen that any new arrangement should be, as far as the signalman was concerned, no different from that already in operation. As a result, his new instrument on which a signalman gave permission to his colleague in the adjacent signalbox for a train to approach, looked almost identical to existing MR pegging instruments. The height of the mahogany case was the same, the needle unit was in the same position as hitherto and only the pegging mechanism on the drop handle was different, with the width of the case increased to accommodate the more complicated mechanical and electrical equipment. Once Train on Line was indicated on the needle, not only was the starting signal of the signalbox in rear locked, but the drop handle of the instrument could not be released until the train had physically passed over a rail-mounted treadle completing the appropriate electrical circuit through the block instrument.

Despite Langdon's work, the impetus for the MR to install lock & block other than as an experiment, only came as a consequence of the disaster on Christmas Eve 1910 at Hawes Junction, an accident which could have been prevented if such equipment had been installed. Ironically, the first trials of a new system, building on Langdon's work, had been made at the beginning of the previous year. Visually the only change from his instrument was the substitution of the drop handle with a rotary commutator and handle. Although the brass ring on the front of the case, engraved with Line Clear, Train on Line and Line Blocked, was impressive, the true elegance of the new instrument lay inside, the electro-mechanical design being both sophisticated and economical. Once the instrument, associated treadles and signal lever locks had proved themselves, hundreds of instruments were manufactured and in 1915, J. Sayers, W. C. Acfield, G. Salt and B. W. Cooke were awarded a full patent for their new Rotary Interlocking Block System (1914, No 9134). The majority of the rotary pegging instruments seem to have been made in 1913, an assumption we are able to make because, unlike any other British railway company, the MR systematically dated its instruments. The earliest date so far found on either an ordinary pegging instrument or a block bell is 1880.

3. Signalling Equipment, Mechanical

The MR was not enthusiastic about interlocking until the very end of the 1860s, having begun that decade by tenaciously resisting pressure from the Railway Inspectorate of the Board of Trade. The switch levers at Oakenshaw Junction installed in 1861, for example, not only had to be held over by the signalman as the train passed through the points but the levers were not interlocked in any way with the junction semaphores. By the middle of the decade, this sort of situation was no longer tolerated by the Railway Inspectorate, and reluctant to pay any inventor for the use of his equipment, the MR produced its first in-house frame design about 1865. It was crude compared with Saxby & Farmer and Stevens & Sons apparatus, and only a few years later it was superseded by a completely new and unique design. This turned out to be a remarkably good piece of engineering which, in all but the type of interlocking between the levers and other minor details, remained in production for nearly one hundred years. The new product pushed the MR into the forefront of lever frame design and it remained, without a doubt, the most functionally compact of any frame put to use on a British railway.

Each lever was pivoted in a separate casting, any number of which could be positioned on a baseplate and fastened together with a pair of tie rods. None of the frame's mechanism had to be positioned below the operating room floor and the locking was neatly housed immediately behind the levers and readily accessible by removing cast cover plates. Frames were usually made up in multiples of four levers and an early standard was the 12-lever frame which was built up on a one-piece cast-iron baseplate. The frame was christened a 'Tumbler' because the locking was activated by rotating tubes called

Above:
The large MR Tumbler frame in Dore & Totley signalbox, 1938. The block shelf also has a good set of standard MR block instruments and bells, including four Rotary Interlocking examples.
Real Photographs/Ian Allan Library

'tumblers'. (This mechanism was completely different from that which gave the same name to LNWR frames.)

Manufacture of the Tumbler Frame must have started before the MR established its purpose-built Signal Works just outside Derby station in 1872, but after that date production was certainly increased. The MR was obviously confident in its product, so much so that in 1873 it preferred to pay Saxby & Farmer royalties for the use of catch-handle locking than redesign any part of its frame. Nevertheless, various features were modified in the light of experience in 1892 and then between 1906 and 1909 a number of frames were turned out with tappet locking. Having proved successful, further modifications were made to reduce the number of parts, and the new tappet frames were produced in large numbers for new and replacement work until the Grouping of 1923. Even then the basic design lived on in subsequent LMS (Rail Executive Committee design, see page 46) and British Rail frames.

4. Signalbox Design

As stated above, the MR was reluctant to use interlocking lever frames until the mid-1860s, which meant that until then there was no need for anything larger than a hut to shelter signalmen whilst on duty. As traffic demands and the Board of Trade forced the pace of change, signalling stages began to appear at MR junctions, and by the end of the 1860s the company was using contractors to build Saxby-type signalboxes in a variety of materials. The first of these structures to incorporate design features that were to remain the hallmark of MR signalboxes until the Grouping made their appearance in 1869/70. Because hundreds of these new signalboxes were required as block working and interlocking was brought into use all over the MR network, they were constructed quickly of prefabricated wooden sections made at Derby Works. All signalboxes had hipped and slate covered roofs with one or two wooden finials depending on whether the roof was square or rectangular in plan. The operating room

Above:
Wellingborough Station signalbox photographed in the late 1930s. The signalbox was not quite an MR standard. The end nearest the photographer was basically of Type 2b pattern except for the position of the door, and the opposite end (invisible here) was of the Type 3a pattern. In addition, apart from the two vertically boarded sections that can be seen between the operating windows, the box was unusual in being glazed on all sides. *R. Atkins*

windows were made up of sash units, two panes high by four panes wide on all but the door elevation, which used sash units only two panes wide. The corners of the top pair of panes were angled to form a neat chamfer, a characteristic of all MR signalboxes from then onwards.

The majority of these Type 1 signalboxes built between 1869/70 and 1883 were small and often square in plan. After 1884, the windows on the front of the operating room were enlarged by the addition of another row of glass panes at the bottom of the sashes and compared to Type 1 signalboxes, post-1884 structures were invariably longer, having to accommodate longer lever frames to control more signals and more complex track layouts.

From then onwards until the Grouping, MR signalbox design remained basically unchanged. There were alterations, but many were so subtle one wonders why the MR bothered. Some changes seem merely cosmetic, others, such as the increase in the size of the operating room windows, were practical improvements. After 1900 the windows on the end elevations on new signalboxes were increased so that they were the same size as those on the front. For a brief period some signalboxes were built with windows with fewer panes, the previous arrangement of four smaller panes in the lower two-thirds of the sash units being replaced by one large sheet of glass. Inexplicably, the glazing of many subsequent signalboxes reverted to the older pattern with all panes of equal size.

Notwithstanding these minor detail differences, of all the pre-Grouping companies, the MR undoubtedly achieved a higher degree of signalbox standardisation than any other, with only a handful of Type 1 boxes still in use by 1923. By then, the MR calculated, it had 1,203 signalboxes, all of which were instantly recognisable as Derby products.

LANCASHIRE & YORKSHIRE RAILWAY

1. Signals

One of the constituent companies of the L&Y was the East Lancashire Railway (ELR), absorbed in 1859. Its Rule Book issued in October 1854 recorded that the Time Interval system was being maintained with flags, semaphores and 'Stationary Signals of various shapes'. Red, green and white flags were used to indicate the standard danger, caution and all-clear signals during the day, with coloured lights in use at night. By comparison, the semaphores were capable of displaying only white or green, there being no mention of the danger position, and the other fixed signals could show only a red or green indication. It is not too fanciful to interpret this as a deliberate policy to keep footplate crews alert. Many railway companies believed very strongly that signals undermined a driver's responsibility for his train, and as if to reinforce this view, the ELR's Rule No 23 specifically mentioned that although crews were '. . . to pay immediate attention to all Signals . . . [they] . . . must not, however, trust to Signals'.

By the end of the century, L&Y drivers had to be some of the most vigilant anywhere in the country because, according to the Signal Engineer, H. Rayner Wilson, they encountered more signals per mile of track than on any other British railway. He calculated the L&Y had 11,511 signals for 529 miles of track, compared with the LNWR which had 14,693 signals for 1,862 miles. Rayner Wilson wrote at a time when the L&Y had achieved a high degree of standardisation in all its mechanical signalling apparatus, but this had not always been the case. Between the 1850s and 1880s, the L&Y had brought into use a variety of equipment depending on the signalling contractor employed at the time.

By the Grouping, however, two standard designs of lower quadrant semaphores were in use. The most characteristic of these was that derived directly from George Edwards' late 1870s pattern manufactured originally by the Gloucester Wagon Co and later by his own company, The Railway Signal Co. This semaphore was one of the first (if not the first) to have the arm attached to the cast spectacle to help counter-balance the whole assembly so that if a rod or wire broke, the arm would assume the danger position. The original design had only one circular lens for the red glass, but the final L&Y pattern had two beehive-shaped glasses following the adoption of green as the all-clear indication after 1893. The alignment of the spectacle with the arm gave the signal a characteristic hooked appearance more pronounced than in any other lower quadrant design. The second standard L&Y semaphore was less unconventional.

Above:
The photographer recorded that this L&Y distant signal on the down line at Thones Bridge was manufactured by the Gloucester Wagon Co. This is particularly interesting because the signal was a direct development of that firm's earlier single glass spectacle design, probably the very first British semaphore with a combined arm and spectacle. After 1893 twin glass spectacles of the pattern shown here were turned out for use by the L&Y, reinforcing the characteristic hooked profile of the original.
Author's collection

Above:
One of the L&Y's more conventional lower quadrant semaphores, photographed at Moorside & Wardley in July 1963. *D. Hampson courtesy J. A. Peden collection*

2. Signalling Equipment, Electrical

The L&Y began to regulate the movement of trains using the block system in the 1850s. At the end of that decade, almost 200 instruments to the design of a Mr Highton were in use and by the beginning of the 1860s one observer reported that '. . . the Lancashire & Yorkshire Company's system of telegraph signalling . . . was very complete, so far as regarded the breaking up into short circuits; and it was difficult to imagine how the trains would get on at all without the aid of electricity, for they were frequently behind time'.

Almost nothing is currently known about Mr Highton and his instruments, nor when they disappeared from L&Y signalboxes. There is more evidence for the use of equipment patented by W. H. Preece and E. Tyer. An engraving of the interior of Hoist Cabin (signalbox), Wakefield, which was published in *The Railway Magazine* in 1898, clearly shows Preece's 1862 block equipment. There is also pictorial evidence for Tyer & Co's apparatus despite the fact the L&Y was not listed as one of this firm's clients in its 1874 catalogue. An official railway company photograph taken in 1920 shows an example of Tyer's one-wire two-position miniature semaphore instrument with Line Clear/Train on Line flap. Another official photograph of 1920 shows a set of three-wire, three-position single-needle instruments, both for absolute and permissive block working. Photographs of signalbox interiors and instruments which survive that are clearly marked L&YR also prove that Tyer's co-operative permissive instruments were widely used on the company's goods lines. Another official company photograph of 1920 shows a variant of Tyer's one-wire, three-position needle instrument which had been patented only the year before (1919 No 126225). In the standard Tyer's design, the needles pointed downwards to the three descriptions, but, so that they conformed with other railway company equipment, the needles of L&Y block instruments were installed so they pointed upwards to their descriptions.

Despite this array of off-the-shelf instrumentation the L&Y, like the LNWR, still felt justified in both designing and manufacturing its own unique style of double-needle absolute block instrument in the last years of the 19th century. The new instrument in the obligatory mahogany case incorporated everything necessary to control a stretch of double track except the block bell which remained a separate piece of equipment.

3. Signalling Equipment, Mechanical

When the Board of Trade began to press for the installation of interlocking equipment at junctions in the 1860s, the L&Y was one of the few northern companies which was held up as a good example by the Railway Inspectorate. During the summer of 1861, the MR's arrangements at its junction with the L&Y at Oakenshaw were criticised by the inspecting officer, and compared directly and unfavourably with those of the L&Y. The L&Y's junction stage and signals were described as superior to those of the MR. What also impressed the inspector was the company's willingness to install a Stevens & Sons frame when asked to do so.

In 1873 the Regulation of Railways Act obliged all railway companies to report to the Board of Trade on progress made with interlocking and block working, and when the statistics were returned for

Left:
Unfortunately the location of this signalbox was not recorded, but it is a very good illustration of a large frame almost certainly made at the L&Y's Horwich Works to The Railway Signal Co's Tappet/Flat Baseplate pattern. Worthy of note, although not from a design point of view, is the fact this is not a posed photograph. The concentration on the face of the Edwardian signalman is obviously genuine. *Author's collection*

1875 the L&Y recorded that 80% of all its connections with passenger lines were interlocked. Apart from the District, North London and Metropolitan railways, no other main-line company came close to this figure. By 1882 the work had been completed — an enviable record.

All this work had been achieved by employing signalling contractors. Rayner Wilson maintained that this was more economical than manufacturing in-house, but the disadvantage with competitive tendering was the inevitable variety of equipment acquired. When the L&Y's impressive Board of Trade return of 1882 was submitted, the company had Stevens & Sons tappet frames in use, a number of Anderson's 1864 Patent frames, examples of Smith's 1870 Patent frames, Saxby & Farmer's 1871 Patent Rocker frames and their successor the 1874 Patent Rocker & Gridiron, and Gloucester Wagon Co frames made to George Edwards' patent of 1877 (No 947). All this equipment fulfilled its purpose, but it meant the L&Y had to have access to a multitude of parts for routine maintenance and alterations.

By the beginning of the 1880s, the L&Y was keen to standardise, and it was this desire which led directly to the establishment of The Railway Signal Co. In 1878 George Edwards, who had previously worked for Saxby & Farmer and the LNWR and currently managed the Gloucester Wagon Co's signalling department, had secured for his employers a five-year exclusive signalling contract with the L&Y. When this was terminated in 1881, the Gloucester Wagon Co asked him to renegotiate with the railway company, but instead he used it as an opportunity to secure an exclusive new contract between himself and the L&Y. On the strength of this he set up his own business trading as The Railway Signal Co Ltd with a new works next to the L&Y at Fazakerley. From the Gloucester Wagon Co he took both his patented lever frame design and his old firm's signalbox design. Always ambitious, in 1884 he substituted tappet locking for his own design, and was the first manufacturer after Stevens & Sons to do so. The flat baseplates variation of his design was installed at various places on the L&Y and from 1889 until the company was absorbed by the LNWR in 1922, it was manufactured at the L&Y's Horwich Works, the castings prominently displaying the railway company and works name.

Above:
The Saxby & Farmer Type 6 pattern signalbox at Hopwood, L&Y. This was the signalling contractor's earliest standardised design built between 1869 and the mid-1870s for companies in the north of England. The small decorative eaves brackets were a particular feature of this design. *Ian Allan Library*

Above:
In the 1870s the L&Y also employed the local signalling firm run by Messrs Yardley and Smith of Manchester, and Waterhouse Siding was one of that firm's first signalbox designs built between 1872 and 1878. *J. A. Peden collection*

Confident in its mechanical signalling practices, the L&Y was one of a number of railway companies in the Edwardian period to try power signalling. The LNWR and the GER were the first to experiment, closely followed by the LSWR, NER and GCR. Of all the possible sources of power, the L&Y chose electro-pneumatic, buying equipment from the Westinghouse Brake Co in 1903. The location selected for the first installation was the west end of the enlarged Bolton station where a new signalbox was erected and fitted with the control equipment. The latter took the place of a mechanical lever frame, but above it was positioned a standard block shelf with the railway company's own design of absolute block instruments and block bells, and a set of Tyer's permissive instruments. The control equipment was an American design which in its original form would have had a row of handles along the front for operating the circuits which drove the point and signal pneumatic cylinders. On the Bolton frame 77 miniature levers were substituted for the handles so that the equipment was not completely alien to Lancashire signalmen. The same type of equipment was brought into use 20 years later at Southport.

4. Signalbox Design

Stevens & Sons built a number of the L&Y's first signalboxes, some all timber, others on brick or stone bases. When the upgrading of signalling gathered pace in the 1870s, the L&Y employed a number of other contractors, all of whom erected new signalboxes of their own design. The local Manchester firm of E. S. Yardley & Co (William Smith from 1876), built brick-based boxes in this period, all but the last design sporting hipped roofs. Saxby & Farmer also won contracts and the most common signalbox design used on the L&Y in the 1870s was what the Signalling Study Group classified as S&F Type 6. This was a plain brick structure with hipped and slate-covered roof, with operating room windows just two panes high, made up into sash units of either four or six panes. This

Left:
Douglas Bank was an example of the final standard signalbox design manufactured and erected by the L&Y. With 18 operating room window sash units it would have been classified a Size 13 by the company. The design was almost identical to that produced by The Railway Signal Co with the exception that the barge boards were plain and not decorative.
B. G. Barlow courtesy Jim Peden

design developed first into the S&F Type 7 when a row of additional windows only one pane deep was inserted beneath the operating room sashes, and then into the Type 8 by the addition of narrow top-lights which had already been used on other Saxby & Farmer designs. A further development which the firm used for a number of its L&Y contracts was the S&F Type 9, which was to all intents and purposes a version for northern railway clients of the firm's Type 5 which was always associated with the LBSCR. The S&F Type 9 was a handsome building usually built with a brick base with prominent overhanging hipped roof and decorative wooden eaves brackets.

The Gloucester Wagon Co built its standard signalboxes on the L&Y, recognisable by their row of additional sashes one pane high by two panes wide immediately below the main operating room windows and the roof gable ends adorned with a distinctive decorative barge board. This design was, of course, perpetuated with minor modifications by the new Railway Signal Co from 1881, examples appearing all over the L&Y system.

When the L&Y's new Horwich Works opened in 1889, not only lever frames but signalbox timber components were manufactured there, The Railway Signal Co's design, minus the decorative barge board, being adopted as the new standard. Both all-timber and brick-based signalboxes were built to this new design and as with the LNWR, the L&Y classified the size of signalboxes by the number of operating room window sash units they incorporated on the front of the structure. A standard sash unit was two panes wide by two panes high. The classification started at 1, for a signalbox with six sashes on the trackside elevation making the structure 14ft 1³/₈in long, and ended at size number 18, for a signalbox 51ft 3¹/₄in long with 23 sash units.

CALEDONIAN RAILWAY

1. Signals

In line with many railway companies south of the border, the CR's early fixed signals were painted boards, which could be rotated to give two positive indications — red for stop and green for caution. The all-clear indication was made by positioning the board so that it could not be seen by approaching trains. By at least the 1860s, the company was using semaphore signals at stations with board signals relegated to serve as distance or auxiliary signals. Whilst the board signals of most railways were simple functional pieces of equipment, those used by the CR were more stylish. There were a number of different designs, all with the lamp attached to the top of the post. The boards used on the Southern Division were oval shaped, pierced by a number of holes and with a rectangular extension on one side. When the red side faced the driver, this extension appeared on the track side of the board, and when the green face was displayed the extension pointed away from the line. On the Central Division, two styles of board were used. One was shaped something like a flat fish, whilst the other was rectangular with straight edges top and bottom and a double reverse curve at either end. The latter board was pieced by a pair of four holes arranged like the petals of a flower. On the Northern Division the board signals were oval with a central circular section pierced by six holes and two protruding rectangular arms at either end.

As block working spread throughout the CR in the 1870s, the company abandoned board distant signals in order to conform with Board of Trade requirements to use semaphores with a V-shape cut from the end of the arms. Having patronised the firm of Stevens & Sons since at least the late 1860s, when that firm had set up a works in Glasgow, the CR continued to install Stevens equipment. When the firm abandoned slot-in-the-post signals and began to produce semaphores with the wooden arms bolted directly to the spectacle castings, these were adopted by the CR. The design of spectacles chosen by the CR had generous glasses, the blue glass for producing the green all-clear indication being slightly larger than the red. Lattice posts, championed by Stevens for many years, also became a company standard, with bracket signals made up from simple wrought-iron straps rather than the more substantial (and presumably more expensive) castings or fabrications preferred by Saxby & Farmer, McKenzie & Holland, and the LNWR, for example.

Above:
A pair of CR lower quadrant signals. The metal lattice posts and finials were standard Stevens & Sons products. The style of twin glass spectacle on both full-size and miniature arms, however, was unique to the CR. Clearly visible are the slots incorporated into both castings to allow subtle positioning on the arms.
Ian Allan Library

2. Signalling Equipment, Electrical

Currently, less is known about the early use of the electric telegraph on the CR than on equivalent English railways, and more research is needed before a complete picture can be formed. What is known is the use by the early 1860s of Cooke & Wheatstone's instruments for sending general railway messages along the line between Glasgow and Paisley, jointly operated with the Glasgow & South Western Railway. At the same time, Highton's single-needle instruments, developed for the L&Y, were also in use.

By the beginning of the 1870s, the CR was using both single-needle block instruments and bells in the familiar three-wire system, as well as Tyer & Co's one-wire instruments. The CR purchased the latter firm's standard two-position miniature semaphore instruments attached to a vertical board supporting a separate plunger at the bottom and either a bell for signalling up trains or a gong for signalling down trains at the top. Sometime in the 1870s, Tyer & Co produced the standard indicating instrument of this set with a mechanical device fitted into the left-hand side of the case capable of indicating IN or OUT. This in effect provided the third indication of Train on Line. The CR used instruments with this feature, but whether they were in use as early as the 1870s is not known.

The next modification to this instrument was the replacement of the separate plunger box by a tapper which was made integral with the main instrument. The block bell or gong still remained a separate unit positioned over the main instrument, but after the modification it was easier to place the whole arrangement on a block shelf over the lever frame. The next design alteration was both a logical and almost inevitable one, and that was the incorporation of the block bell and/or gong into the top of the main instrument case. By this means the back board was done away with altogether, but it meant that the new instrument that emerged was over 2ft tall, making it the largest one-piece block instrument then available.

Aesthetically, the instrument looked top heavy, with a large expanse of French-polished mahogany above the miniature semaphores. This is not merely the judgement of the author. It must also have concerned either the manufacturer or the railway company as well, because a larger-than-necessary brass plate, engraved with the name of the signalbox to which the instrument was connected, was fitted on just this part of the instrument (see p71).

3. Signalling Equipment, Mechanical

By the time the Board of Trade was able to oblige railway companies to install the block system and interlocking on all new lines built after 1871, the CR was the only Scottish railway company which compared favourably with English railways in the use of the latest signalling equipment. By the end of 1875, the CR had interlocked 67% of all connections with passenger lines compared to 69% achieved by its West Coast partner, the LNWR. To put both these figures into perspective, the Glasgow & South Western Railway, the CR's nearest Scottish rival in the Board of Trade interlocking league tables, scored only 39%.

Over the years, the CR patronised Saxby & Farmer and The Railway Signal Co, but it was Stevens & Sons which had the most influence over signalling matters, in both the design of semaphores (as outlined above) and the type of lever frames. The CR was one of the first to install examples of Stevens' pioneering interlocking lever frame developed in 1860. This patronage must have helped persuade the firm to set up a new works in Glasgow, which began to turn out frames with tappet locking patented in the Stevens name in 1870 (No 746). This design, subsequently christened Stevens Glasgow Old Pattern by the Signalling Study Group in the 1980s, differed in details from its English counterpart and was supplied only to railways north of the border. Stevens equipment remained popular in Scotland long after English railways had turned to other signalling contractors, an observation reinforced by the fact that in the mid-1890s Stevens made frame design modifications which were not incorporated into its English counterpart. A few years after this, the CR began to manufacture its own variant of the frame at its St Rollox works, a design which has become known as the Stevens/Caledonian pattern. After the Grouping of 1923, manufacture continued and the design became the standard for all LMS lines in Scotland. Production continued into British Railway days until the early 1960s, after which frames were assembled from second-hand parts, the last appearing in 1984.

4. Signalbox Design

The first standard signalboxes to appear on the CR during the 1870s were brick-based structures with hipped and slated roofs. The design used on the Northern Division changed very little from then until the Grouping. On the first examples, built from the 1870s until the beginning of the 1890s, the operating room windows were made up of discrete sash units three panes high by three panes wide. From then

Left:
Curriehill was one of the CR's Southern Division Type 1 signalboxes, the type which was closest in style to those used between 1870 and 1890 on the Northern Division. By the time this photograph was taken in 1956, the central decorative roof finial had been removed. *I. S. Pearsall*

Above:
The impressive CR Type S4 at Kirtlebridge Junction, photographed in 1931.
Locomotive & General Railway Publishing

until the beginning of the 20th century, the width of each sash unit was reduced by one pane, making the sashes appear taller and nearer in style to the windows of Southern Division boxes. For a short period from about 1902 to 1908, signalboxes were erected with operating window sashes three panes wide again, but lacking the bottom horizontal glazing bar.

On the Southern Division hipped roofs were also the norm, covered with either slate tiles or zinc sheets, but although some of the earliest 1870s signalboxes had operating room window sash units with the same number and distribution of panes as their northern equivalents, there were many that did not conform and differed in other details. The most distinctive Southern Division design, the features of which did become standardised, was classified as the Type S4 by later signalling historians. It had a long life, first appearing in the 1870s and continuing to be erected until the Grouping. Both masonry and timber examples were built, the most striking feature being the prominent overhang to the roof on all elevations, this overhang connected by large decorative brackets to vertical timbers which separated each sash unit of the operating room windows. Each sash was usually made up of just two panes, the horizontal glazing bar aligning with the base of the decorative brackets.

GLASGOW & SOUTH WESTERN RAILWAY

1. Signals

Of the many designs of early fixed signals, those used by the G&SWR were particularly unusual. According to W. E. Edwards, who wrote a series of articles on early signals which were published in the 1904 *Railway Magazine*, the G&SWR shared the distinction with its neighbour the North British Railway on its Edinburgh and Glasgow line and, at the other end of the country, the GWR of using a signal which could display a positive 'all-clear' as well as a danger indication. All-clear on the majority of railway companies was achieved with no visible indication. The G&SWR signal consisted of three circular discs fitted at right-angles to a T-shaped armature. Two red-coloured discs were aligned at 90° to a third which was painted green. The armature could be rotated so that either the pair of red discs or the single green one faced oncoming trains. Edwards recorded that, unlike other railway companies, green was used as an all-clear not a caution indication, white being used on the reverse of all three discs as a neutral colour.

By the beginning of the 1870s, however, when a number of these devices were ending their useful lives as auxiliary/distant signals, green had reverted to its more usual association with the caution indication. The MR's 1871 Rule Book which had diagrams of many board signals used by other companies included one of the G&SWR pattern. Confusingly, there was a note under the illustration which read: 'When indicating "All Right", these Signals are turned so as to present the edge to the approaching Driver.'

Less ambiguous were the indications of contemporary three-position semaphores which the G&SWR had adopted for use at stations. Along with its neighbours, the NBR and the CR, G&SWR signalling was by then heavily influenced by the manufacturer and contractor Stevens & Sons, and that firm's lattice signal posts and other standard fittings were used widely. When semaphore signals, with the arm fixed to the spectacle casting, began to replace the earlier slot-in-the-post design in the 1890s, the G&SWR installed Stevens & Sons' new combined pattern. The railway company also adopted a variant of that firm's standard spectacle casting in which the red glass was circular and the blue/green glass was a slightly larger oval.

When the G&SWR resignalled Glasgow St Enoch station in 1902, a reversion was made to fixing semaphore arms for up and down directions on the same post. The impressive signal gantry there, spanning all tracks, was fitted with 12 lattice posts (dolls), each supporting two arms (three of these dolls were also fitted with an extra single arm). This saved the expense of erecting 12 extra dolls, and costs were reduced further by the provision of only one lamp for every pair of arms, the lamp being fitted inside the post.

As a postscript to G&SWR signal design, St Enoch station was also the first location in the country to be fitted with what later became known as Sykes' 'banner repeaters'. At St Enoch these signals were used to control shunting movements, installed when the station was resignalled by the W R. Sykes Interlocking Signal Co in 1898. The design was modified in the light of experience and patented by the firm in 1909 (No 6145). After the Grouping they were used by all the 'Big Four' railway companies to repeat the indication of signals that could not be seen, for any variety of reasons, at a safe braking distance by approaching drivers.

2. Signalling Equipment, Electrical

Similarly to the CR, the G&SWR turned to Tyer & Co when it needed to introduce block working at the beginning of the 1870s. At that time, much was made of the savings to be enjoyed by adopting Tyer's one-wire momentary current equipment, compared to the older three-wire continuous current systems derived from Cooke & Wheatstone's needle telegraph. In the 1870s and '80s Tyer's standard twin miniature semaphore instruments, fitted on to back boards with block bell and separate plunger, were installed in pairs in G&SWR signalboxes controlling double-track through lines. Whilst block working based on the two indications of Line Clear and Train on Line remained in force, Tyer's equipment was reliable and cost-effective. From the mid-1890s, however, when the third position of Line Blocked became part of the Railway Clearing House standard block signalling procedures, the G&SWR looked to Tyer & Co to provide an economical one-wire instrument capable of displaying three indications. There must have been some co-operation between manufacturer and user on the redesign, because although the G&SWR could have installed the same modified type as used by the CR, it chose a completely different design. In place of the twin plungers on the main instrument (one for raising the miniature semaphore arm, the other for lowering it), a single plunger passing through the centre of a circular commutator working a pointer was substituted. The plunger raised or lowered the

Above:
The signal gantry at the east end of the G&SWR's St Enoch station, Glasgow. The signals shown were erected in 1902 as part of the electro-mechanical resignalling by W. R. Sykes Interlocking Co of Clapham, London. The signals were electrically operated. Below them were Sykes 'banner signals' first used at St Enoch in 1898.
Westinghouse Brake & Signal Co

semaphore arm depending on which of the three indications the pointer pointed to. To distinguish between Train on Line and Line Blocked, when the miniature arms were raised, a small screen with 'On Line' appeared behind a circular window next to each arm when Train on Line had been signalled. For the Line Blocked indication, the screen was blank.

As with all Tyer & Co one-wire equipment of this date, although the block bell (or gong), twin needle or miniature semaphore instrument and separate plunger were usually fitted on to one back board, all could be mounted separately on a block shelf. Nevertheless, in the first decade of the 20th century, Tyer & Co designed for both the CR and the G&SWR an instrument with the three main components (incorporating each railway company's detail differences) fitted into one large wooden case. Although significant numbers of these new 'combined' instruments had appeared in the signalboxes of both companies by the Grouping, hundreds of original instruments remained in use.

Above:
The G&SWR Type 1 signalbox at Annan, opened in 1876. *J. Critchley*

3. Signalling Equipment, Mechanical

As mentioned in the CR section of this chapter, the G&SWR was slow in providing interlocking at its junctions and stations. In 1868 a large Stevens & Sons frame with tappet locking was installed at Kilmarnock but 10 years later only 61% of all connections with passenger-carrying lines had been interlocked, and it was not until 1893 that 100% was achieved. As with most Scottish railway companies, Stevens & Sons was the preferred contractor. Stevens Glasgow Old Pattern frames with tappet locking were installed during the 1870s and from the 1880s the firm manufactured components which were assembled by the G&SWR at its Irvine works. In the 1890s Stevens modified its standard design to satisfy the differing requirements of the CR and the G&SWR, the former actually manufacturing as well as assembling, the latter continuing to buy components for assembly.

In the first decade of the 20th century the G&SWR was one of the railways caught up in the fad for power signalling. When St Enoch station, Glasgow, was enlarged, the company turned to the W. R. Sykes Interlocking Co of Clapham, London, to supply and install its recently patented electro-mechanical signalling equipment (1901, No 7067). To operate the points, 88 standard mechanical levers were used, but to save space, a row of pull-out slides to operate the signals electrically was fitted over this frame. After the points had been moved to set a particular route, a 'routing' or 'key' lever was reversed or put back to the normal position in the frame, depending on the route to be signalled, which unlocked the signal slides. Facing point lock levers were dispensed with and point levers were electrically locked whilst a train passed over them. Four other signalboxes on the approaches to the station were similarly equipped.

4. Signalbox Design

With little interlocking until the 1870s, the G&SWR had no distinctive signalboxes until that decade. When a standard design did begin to appear it was an all-timber one. It changed little over the years, all variants (the Signalling Study Group in the 1970s identified seven distinct types) having hipped roofs covered with slates. The most obvious progression was an increase in the size of glass panes in the operating room windows. Until the mid-1880s the windows were small and there was prominent boarding between the top of the sashes and the eaves of the roof. Then for the next 25 years this boarding disappeared and the windows were enlarged. This change, and the abandoning of vertical glazing bars on a number of designs, had the effect of making the signalboxes stark, almost 'modern' in appearance. From the beginning of the 20th century, the boarding between the windows and the eaves reappeared, but the use of even larger sheets of glass still made the signalboxes appear very utilitarian.

HIGHLAND RAILWAY

1. Signals

For many years signalling on the Highland Railway (HR) was minimal, and it was not until the 1890s that standards began to improve. Unlike other Scottish companies, the HR initially turned to McKenzie & Holland to supply its mechanical equipment, and that firm's standard semaphore arms, fabricated brackets and wooden posts with distinctive cast-iron umbrella finials began to appear at stations.

2. Signalling Equipment, Electrical

The electric telegraph was used to regulate the passage of trains over the HR's predominantly single lines for many years after Tyer's Electric Train Tablet System had become available from the end of the 1870s. When the railway company eventually installed Tyer's equipment in 1899, it also brought James Manson's automatic tablet exchange apparatus into use at the same time (details in the Great North of Scotland Railway section of the LNER chapter).

Above:
The signal brackets at the HR station of Forres, photographed in 1934. The characteristic McKenzie & Holland finials indicate that this Worcester signalling contractor was responsible for the work. Note the 'bow-tie' semaphore arms with their 'Ss' for controlling shunting on the 'wrong road'. *Locomotive & General Railway Publishing*

Above:
The decoration on the barge boards indicates that the other famous Worcester signalling contractor, Dutton & Co, provided this signalbox at Helmsdale. Samuel Dutton had worked for many years for McKenzie & Holland before setting up his own business in 1888. Helmsdale was an example of the special HR variant of this firm's Type 1 signalbox, the porch incorporated as part of the roof being the most distinctive feature. *R. E. Ruffell*

3. Signalling Equipment, Mechanical

The HR was slow to introduce interlocking and took a long time to protect the whole network. By 1885 only 50% of all connections between points and signals on passenger lines had been interlocked, and what forced the pace of change was the 1889 Regulation of Railways Act. Even then, full compliance with the requirements of the Act was not achieved until the end of the century.

As mentioned above, the contractor McKenzie & Holland did most of the initial work for the company in the 1880s. Depending on when the work was carried out, the firm installed its current frame design. In the 1890s Dutton & Co Ltd was also used by the HR for resignalling projects, so that firm's standard lever frames were installed.

4. Signalbox Design

The first signalboxes on the HR were built to the signalling contractor's basic design, the only differences compared to McKenzie & Holland or Dutton & Co's all-timber pattern being the use of vertical battened boarding in place of horizontal weatherboarding, and corrugated iron roofs instead of slate. After 1900, the HR built signalboxes to its own unpretentious design with brick locking rooms and gabled roofs covered with slate tiles.

NORTH STAFFORDSHIRE RAILWAY

1. Signals

The first mention of signals in use on the North Staffordshire Railway (NSR) comes from the company's own Rules & Regulations Book of March 1848. Reference is made to semaphores worked to the then standard three positions with 5min intervals between each indication.

The success of the signalling contractor McKenzie, Clunes & Holland was due in no small part to the patronage of the NSR at the end of the 1860s, and it was this firm's semaphores which were erected at stations and junctions in this period. The first designs were the usual slot-in-the-post variety with the cast spectacle located below the arm, sometimes many feet below. This design was improved after the GNR's Abbotts Ripton accident of 1876 by pivoting the arm on the face of the square-sectioned timber post, but it was not until the following decade that the spectacle was attached to the end of the arm to create the final form of signal. What is particularly interesting is the way in which this was done. There is little doubt that the type of spectacle used by the GNR was identical to that supplied to the NSR. This is not surprising as McKenzie & Holland was one of the GNR's preferred contractors. The way in which the GNR somersault signal worked meant the spectacle could not be attached to the end of the arm, but in the case of NSR signals it could. Photographs clearly show that when McKenzie & Holland brought the arm and spectacle together, although the latter was not designed to fit securely on the arm, rather than go to the expense of redesigning the spectacle, the firm simply fitted two additional blocks to the arm to prevent the spectacle moving and becoming misaligned.

2. Signalling Equipment, Electrical

Just as the NSR remained loyal to one supplier for all its mechanical signalling needs, so it continued to purchase its electrical block equipment from one firm. Tyer & Co's standard one-wire, two-position block instruments were installed in all NSR signalboxes in the 1870s and remained in use until the first decade of the 20th century. After this, the NSR implemented a programme of replacing the equipment with Tyer's new one-wire three-position needle instruments which had been patented by the firm in 1902 (No 9284). These had an even longer life and remained in use until the 1970s, removed not because they were worn out, but for the sake of uniformity.

3. Signalling Equipment, Mechanical

During the late 1860s and early 1870s, when the railway company was systematically interlocking its junctions and stations, McKenzie & Holland had a monopoly of that signalling work. Initially the firm used frames made to its 1866 patent (No 1963), a particularly successful mechanism which confirmed the firm's position as the chief rival to Saxby & Farmer and Stevens & Sons. In 1873 another patent was secured (No 2034) which established the characteristic appearance of all subsequent McKenzie & Holland frames, and it was frames of this design which enabled the NSR to complete its programme of interlocking by 1880.

Further McKenzie & Holland design improvements followed in 1886 and c1893, lever frames of these designs being installed in the latest NSR Type 2 signalboxes replacing either earlier and smaller signalboxes or older interlocking equipment.

4. Signalbox Design

No illustrations of the NSR's first signalboxes have come to light. The first known structures date from the 1870s and were built to McKenzie & Holland's

Right:
A McKenzie & Holland bracket signal at the NSR's Heath Junction, photographed in 1958. The fabricated support for the landing stage was a typical product of that firm, the same pattern appearing on other English railways, most notably the NER. *Pamlin Prints*

Above:
Another McKenzie & Holland product for the NSR — the down distant at Trentham Junction. Note the GNR-style twin glass spectacle and the additional reinforcement above and below the spur attaching it to the semaphore arm. *Pamlin Prints*

Below:
An example of a McKenzie & Holland Type 1 signalbox provided for the NSR at Blythe Bridge. *M. R. Henney*

Type 1 design. This was a solid structure with brick base, hipped roof and small operating room windows made up of sash units two panes wide by two panes high. Above these windows there was a prominent boarded section of horizontal timbers approximately half the height of the sash units. Windows in the locking room were either wooden rectangular casements set within a domestic-style stone lintel and sill, or cast-iron factory-style windows with semi-circular tops.

From about 1875, the NSR started to use a design which was almost identical to the Type 1b/1875 drawing (Yorks & Notts) being constructed by the GNR in the same period. This may be no coincidence as most of the GNR boxes of this design were put up by McKenzie & Holland on that company's Staffordshire Extension Railway which connected directly with the NSR. The characteristic of both designs was the fitting of a decorative barge board on each gable end which, like those on GNR signalboxes, varied in form. Almost invariably on NSR signalboxes it was echoed in miniature on the porch on the landing at the top of the outside staircase.

This NS Type 1 signalbox design was eventually superseded in the middle of the 1880s by one which had many characteristics in common with McKenzie & Holland's own Type 3 pattern structure. Both designs had brick bases with a section of horizontal timber boarding beneath operating room windows made up of sash units two panes wide by three panes high, and a glazed porch at the top of the staircase. Where they differed was in the pitch of the gabled roof, that on the NSR structures being steeper, and the barge board, which on NSR signalboxes extended beyond the end of the roof and had unobtrusive bulbous ends pierced by circular holes.

CHESHIRE LINES COMMITTEE

1. Signals

The earliest semaphores on the Cheshire Lines Committee (CLC) were almost certainly supplied by Stevens & Sons, who continued as a favoured contractor into the 1870s. Where this firm undertook the signalling, its ubiquitous metal lattice signal posts were erected. Elsewhere, square-section timber posts and dolls were used, and at the end of World War 1, in line with a number of other railways, the CLC started to put up concrete posts

Until 1893 white continued to be used as the night-time all-clear indication, but from then on a start was made changing this aspect to a green one. To coincide with this work the CLC designed its own twin glass spectacle for attaching to the end of the wooden semaphore arms. The design was unusual because the division between the two glasses was aligned exactly with the centreline of the arm. As a result, the top red glass and the bottom blue/green glass appeared to protrude the same distance above and below the arm (see p67). In fact, the lower glass was slightly deeper to allow for variations in the inclination of the arm when in the 'off' or all-clear position.

Unlike the majority of the country's Victorian railways, the CLC was not absorbed into one of the 'Big Four' companies in 1923 and continued as an independent organisation until nationalisation of the railways in 1948. It was only in 1936 that the LMS took over responsibility for signalling on the network, which gave the CLC a number of years after World War 1 when it continued to develop its own signalling practices. The most obvious result of this independence was the introduction of an unique upper quadrant semaphore in 1929. This was indeed a defiant gesture when all the 'Big Four' companies, with the notable exception of the GWR, were adopting the same standard upper quadrant arm which, with only minor detail differences, remains the standard today where Railtrack has mechanical signalling in operation. The CLC's new signal was created by the simple expedient of using the existing spectacle casting, turning it over and attaching it to the back of the arm so that the blue/green glass was then at the top. If readers are sceptical, careful examination of photographs shows this.

Above:
CLC upper quadrant semaphores photographed near Cheadle in 1951. Compared with their lower quadrant predecessors, the 'new design' had a longer plate between the arm and spectacle, whilst the same twin glass spectacle was used but turned over and attached to the back of the plate. *W. S. Garth*

2. Signalling Equipment, Electrical

The CLC began to introduce block working systematically on all its lines in the early 1870s and it appears to have favoured three-wire continuous current equipment. The CLC indicating instruments that survive, marked with the company's initials, are of the standard single-needle pattern used by many pre-Grouping railways. The original peg-and-chain arrangement was superseded in the 1880s by Langdon's patent catch mechanism (1884 No 61), indicating the MR's influence on CLC signalling. Unlike standard MR equipment, however, on CLC instruments Line Clear, Line Blocked and Train on Line were painted on the single-needle unit and not on the zinc surround. Block bells were also made to the MR's standard pattern.

Until dial signals to reinforce bell codes were abandoned in 1895, in common with all other railways who used three-wire equipment derived from Cooke & Wheatstone's instruments, CLC pegging and non-pegging block instruments were identical save that the latter had no pegging mechanism. After 1895 the CLC adopted the GNR practice of reducing the size of the non-pegging instrument by using only the top half of the mahogany case which housed the single-needle unit.

Above:
Stevens & Sons provided this CLC signalbox at Baguley in the 1870s. The design was used only on the CLC, but Stevens shaped the ends of the vertical boards in the gable ends in its own characteristic way. The decorative barge boards and curved tops to the operating room window sashes were reminiscent of certain GNR 'boxes. *S. C. Dent*

Above:
West Timperley was an example of the first in-house CLC signalbox design, erected by the company between the 1870s and 1903. *S. C. Dent*

3. Signalling Equipment, Mechanical

Unlike other jointly controlled railways, signalling on the CLC was the responsibility of the company's own Engineer. Stevens & Sons inevitably won the earliest contracts for interlocking at the end of the 1860s, and then various jobs were awarded to Saxby & Farmer and McKenzie & Holland in the following decade. In 1884 The Railway Signal Co won the contract to signal the Southport Extension.

By then, the CLC was already in the process of creating its own signalling works with a capacity for both manufacturing and maintenance. In 1881 a workshop was established at Warrington which by 1883/4 was making both lever frames and fabricating most of the timber components for signalboxes. The CLC's own design of lever frame was based closely on the Stevens tappet pattern and production continued at Warrington until the LMS takeover of signalling in 1936.

4. Signalbox Design

The first signalboxes on the CLC were built by Stevens & Sons at the close of the 1860s. In the early years of the 1870s, a distinct CLC/Stevens design was being erected at various locations. These brick-based structures had the Stevens standard type of gabled, slate-covered roofs with vertical boarding in the gable ends, but with the addition of decorative barge boards very similar to one of the patterns appearing on GNR signalboxes of the same date. Another feature shared in common with a number of GNR signalboxes was the curved tops to the two-pane-wide by three-pane-deep operating room window sash units. Unlike GNR signalboxes, however, the door to the operating room at the top of the external staircase was not part of the wooden superstructure but was pierced into the solid brick wall. Stevens & Sons did not have a complete monopoly of CLC signalling work, however, and where Saxby & Farmer was the contractor, it provided its own standard design of signalbox, that provided at Hale station in the middle of the 1870s, for example, being one of the firm's Type 8 pattern.

Once the Warrington signal works had been brought into use, signalboxes to the CLC's own design began to appear. These vertical boarded timber structures had hipped roofs with generous overhanging eaves and very prominent top-lights above the operating room windows, the panes being the same size as those in the main sash units. Huts were invariably provided at the top of the outside stairs to accommodate the earth closet. The most notable variants of this standard signalbox were the more generous roof overhang supported on decorative wooden brackets the same height as the top lights, and the different distribution of panes in the sash units. A striking feature of most of these CLC Type 1 signalboxes was the large roof ventilator which was a cylindrical metal fabrication with a pointed top.

From 1903 the railway company started to erect signalboxes of a new, simpler design. These structures had gabled roofs, vertical weatherboarding and no top lights. Some were provided with plain barge boards and others with the pattern that had been used by both the Manchester, Sheffield & Lincolnshire Railway (MS&LR) and the GNR in the 1870s. By applying these features to his signalboxes as with the CLC/Stevens/GNR decorative barge boards of the 1870s, the company's Engineer may well have been consciously acknowledging the parent companies responsible for the CLC.

What was completely unique to the majority of CLC signalboxes, however, was the style of lettering used on the single large nameboard attached to the front of every structure just below the operating room windows. Most railways used a utilitarian sans-serif typeface, but the CLC used upper-case lettering with heavy serifs, the first letter of each separate word being a few inches larger than the rest.

FURNESS RAILWAY

1. Signals

Some of the earliest semaphores used on the FR were supplied by Stevens & Sons, mounted on that firm's distinctive metal lattice posts with cast lattice ball and spike finials. The arm, or arms, were pivoted in the usual slot at the top of the post, with the lamp fitted just below the slot. Stevens' standard, and very distinctive, twin aspect cast-iron spectacle was used with a red glass for danger and a blue/green one for caution. All-clear was signalled at night when the spectacle was moved clear of the lamp so that its natural whitish light was displayed. A feature of those early semaphores which the FR also perpetuated on later signals was the provision of lifting apparatus which allowed the lamp to be trimmed and filled at ground level, and then winched into position behind the spectacle.

After the Abbotts Ripton accident on the GNR in 1876, the FR was one of companies which no longer installed slot-in-the-post signals, although older examples continued in use for many more years. The next development was the combining of the semaphore arm with the spectacle, and photographs seem to indicate that the majority of FR signals were of this type by the Grouping of 1923. The FR does not appear to have had its own design of semaphore, being content to use the latest pattern supplied by the various signalling contractors it employed.

FR signalling was no more or less progressive or conservative than the majority of British railway companies, except in one important respect. In the early years of the 20th century there was much debate about whether more should be done to distinguish the distant signal from stop signals, particularly in regard to the night-time indication. A number of railways in the south of England used the Coligny-Welch reflector at the side of distant signal lamps (see p97). Other companies believed it was time to adopt the American system of three-aspect signalling, which meant replacing the red glass on distant signals with one which could display an orange or yellow light. By 1914 this was becoming the preferred option, but in that year the FR took a completely novel approach and experimented with a maritime flashing lamp — Aga Flashlight Signal — which it fitted to six distant signals. The equipment was supplied free of charge by the Gas Accumulator

Above:
An interesting oblique view of an FR slot-in-the-post lower quadrant distant signal at Meathop. The style of spectacle and cast finial (although the top spike was missing from this one) immediately indicate this was a Stevens & Sons standard product.
M. H. Walshaw

Co and then purchased by the FR at the end of the six months trial period. World War 1 stifled any further experiments, and within 10 years the spectacles of distant signals all over the country were being progressively fitted with yellow glasses.

2. Signalling Equipment, Electrical

The FR was one of Edward Tyer's earliest customers, buying his one-wire, two-position instruments for block working from at least the beginning of the 1860s. When Tyer improved his basic design, the FR remained loyal and in the 1870s installed his standard twin miniature semaphore instrument mounted on a back board with the block bell and separate plunger for exchanging bell and gong codes between signalmen without altering the position of the miniature semaphores.

By 1874, Tyer & Co was marketing its standard instrument with a flap attached which was positioned so that when it covered either plunger the other could not be operated (easily). Originally the firm advertised this instrument for the control of single lines, but it was soon used on double lines owned by both the FR and the GER. The FR's appendix to its working timetable of 1905 referred to this flap as a movable 'screen', one side of which was painted red to indicate Train on Line whilst it covered the Line Clear plunger, the other side painted green to indicate Line Clear whilst the Train on Line plunger was covered. This screen was either pivoted horizontally as illustrated in Tyer & Co's 1874 catalogue and as shown in the photograph of the L&Y instruments mentioned earlier in the section on L&Y signalling, or it was placed vertically as the 'flap' fitted to Tyer's one-wire instruments supplied to the GER (see p54).

Photographs from the 1920s of FR signalbox interiors show that the railway company used another style of Tyer's semaphore instruments as well, this pattern fitted with a combined plunger, commutator and indicator, the latter capable of displaying Line Clear, Train on Line and Line Blocked. It was the twin-needle version of this design which Tyer supplied to the LNWR (see page 14).

The final upgrading of FR block working equipment occurred from 1906 onwards when Tyer's one-wire, three-position needle instruments were adopted. These new instruments had been patented by Tyer & Co in 1902 (No 9284). The FR rented the instruments from J. B. Saunders & Co who also maintained them for the railway company. (J. B. Saunders manufactured these instruments to Tyer's Patent and also supplied them to the Taff Vale Railway.) FR block regulations were altered at the same time. Originally, on the twin semaphore instruments, the normal position with no trains travelling between signalboxes was with the semaphores lowered — sometimes described by Victorian engineers as 'open' or 'positive' block working. This position of the semaphore, of course, could also indicate that a train had been accepted and the signalmen had exchanged Line Clear bell codes. Once a train was signalled out of section the bell code was acknowledged with one beat on the Line Clear plunger to lower the semaphore. On the new instruments, the normal indication became Line Blocked, thereby bringing the FR in line with the Railway Clearing House standard block signalling regulations.

3. Signalling Equipment, Mechanical

When the resignalling boom of the 1870s and '80s on Britain's railways was in full swing, the FR, as with the GNR, was prepared to use a number of signalling contractors to fulfil its requirements. In

Right:
The platform starter at Coniston. This signal, as with many on the FR, was fitted with a windlass for raising and lowering the lamp, the pulley wheel fitting into a slot at the top of the post. Behind 0-6-0 No 118 is Coniston signalbox, a nice example of an FR Type 2 with the timber bracing of the superstructure exposed. *Locomotive Publishing Co/ Bucknall Collection/ Ian Allan Library*

Above:
The FR Type 4 signalbox at Arnside. The use of rubble stone instead of brick, and the subtle change of verticals between the operating and locking rooms, gave this particular structure a more 'picturesque' appearance than other Type 4s. *J. Scrace*

the 1870s most FR work went to Easterbrook & Co, but the less well known company of William Baines & Co of Smethwick in Staffordshire also supplied a few lever frames in that decade. In the 1880s it was The Railway Signal Co which won most of the contracts for both new work and the replacement of earlier lever frame designs. It was one of the variants of this firm's tappet frames which became the nearest thing to a FR standard, the design also being made and installed by Evans O'Donnell and F. A. Atkinson when they won FR signalling contracts at the end of the 19th century.

4. Signalbox Design

When the FR started to erect signalboxes in the early 1870s to accommodate interlocked lever frames and block instruments, it used its own designs. The first structures (Type 1) had features in common with current Saxby & Farmer designs — the shallow roofs were hipped and covered with slates, and above the small operating room windows there were narrow top-lights. However, many had rough-cut stone bases which gave them a rustic appearance. From the mid-1870s onwards this was accentuated when the prominent diagonal cross-brace timber framing of the superstructure was left exposed on the exterior. In the centre of the operating room windows there was also a boarded section on to which the Tyer's instruments were attached, and this too had its diagonal cross-brace exposed. On a number of all-timber signalboxes the cross-bracing appeared only on the bases, but, whatever the detail differences were, the prominent bracing was often picked out in a darker colour to the rest of the boarding, giving the boxes a distinctive appearance.

In the 1880s another design appeared (Type 3) which was the closest any British railway company came to building architectural rather than purely functional signalboxes (see p78). The pitch of the hipped roof was increased and clay tiles were used instead of slates. The operating room windows were made up of units with one large sheet of glass and two, three or four smaller panes fitted into the top quarter of these windows. But the most unusual and pleasing feature was the tall tapering base either of ashlar stone or brick pierced by narrow locking room windows. These were reminiscent of arrow-slits and gave the structure the appearance of a mediaeval tower. As this author commented in his *abc Signalboxes* (Ian Allan Publishing, 1997), in many ways this design owed something to the mediaevally inspired work of Victorian architects Anthony Salvin (1799-1881) and William Burges (1827-81).

Unfortunately, these structures must have been more expensive to build than could be justified, because from 1896 onwards, the FR introduced a more conventional design with a slated, hipped roof and either a panelled brick base or, for those more picturesque spots on the line, one constructed of rough-cut stones. The Signalling Study Group classified this sensible design as Type 4.

NORTH LONDON RAILWAY

1. Signals

Little is known about the earliest signals on the North London Railway (NL), but the semaphores used in the 1850s and '60s were almost certainly supplied by Stevens & Sons. In 1877 the NL established a signal works at Bow, and semaphores as well as lever frames were eventually manufactured there. The most distinctive semaphore arm design made by the company was one for use in restricted spaces.

2. Signalling Equipment, Electrical

The NL was one of the early advocates of absolute block working, taking its lead from the SER, and by 1855 all lines were protected by the system. The company was also an early user of Edward Tyer's one-wire equipment, and it may have been some of Tyer's original design of instruments which were brought into use in the mid-1850s. His firm certainly maintained the NL's block equipment from the end of the 1860s until 1884.

As mentioned elsewhere, with the refinement of the block system in the 1880s came the need for instruments capable of displaying three permanent positions. Existing Tyer's customers either struggled on with their original two-position equipment, or started to use instruments fitted with various mechanical devices to give that third indication. The NL followed the LNWR's lead by deciding to abandon the use of one-wire, two position equipment altogether, and in 1895, H. J. Pryce, the company's Signal Superintendent, obtained a patent jointly with L. de M. G. Ferreira (the company's Telegraph Inspector) for a three-wire, three-position needle block instrument. Tyer & Co already marketed such an instrument, but this was yet another example of a British railway company believing there were economies to be made by going it alone. Ironically, Pryce & Ferreira's patent block instrument was manufactured for the NL by Tyer & Co, adding to its already diverse selection of products.

Conversion of the one-wire system and installation of Pryce & Ferreira's instruments was achieved extremely rapidly, with work completed by the end of 1896.

3. Signalling Equipment, Mechanical

The history of railway signalling in this country has many milestones, and one of the most influential was on NL territory. In September 1859, the Railway Inspectorate came to see the arrangements for signalling the new junction at Kentish Town (Camden Road). A Stevens & Sons stirrup frame had been installed to work the signals, a familiar piece of equipment at that date. However, Col Yolland refused to sanction the opening of the new Hampstead Junction Railway until the signals and points were interconnected so that 'contradictory signals' could not be displayed. This was at a time when the use of John Saxby's 1856 patent 'Simultaneous Motion' equipment was being put forward as good practice. Stevens & Sons did some alterations but in the end it was the additions to the stirrup frame devised by the NL's engineer, Austin Chambers, which satisfied the Board of Trade and pushed interlocking into its next important stage of development.

Chambers' breakthrough was devising a mechanism which forced the signalman to carry out a sequence of operations in a set order so that the points were in the correct position before the appropriate semaphore signal could be lowered, and conversely that signals had to be returned to danger before the points could once again be moved. This principle of 'successive motion' was immediately appreciated by Stevens & Sons and John Saxby who applied it to their own lever frame designs. Stevens & Sons had a new frame incorporating new 'successive motion' interlocking in operation by March 1860, and Saxby had his version patented that summer (No 1754).

Although Chambers was rewarded for his work at Kentish Town Junction by NL management and had his apparatus patented, subsequent events very quickly consigned his breakthrough to signalling history. Nevertheless, his company's commitment to interlocking continued throughout the 1860s. In

Above:
A pair of restricted space lower quadrant semaphores of NLR design at Dalston Junction. Behind is the 1872 Dalston Junction No 2 signalbox, extended at the far end in 1908 in exactly the same style, including the decorative awning. *BR(LMR) official photograph*

1865 the comparatively new firm of McKenzie, Clunes & Holland was employed to interlock the NL's London terminus at Broad Street, a task requiring four new signalboxes. Before long the rest of the network had been fully interlocked and in 1873, the first year when every railway was obliged to report progress on interlocking to the Board of Trade, the NL was one of only three companies in the British Isles (the Metropolitan and the District railways were the others) with a 100% record.

In the early 1870s many stretches of line were quadrupled and most of the new interlocking work was carried out by Stevens & Sons, Saxby & Farmer, McKenzie & Holland and Easterbrook & Co. By the end of the decade, however, the usual disadvantages of being amongst the first in a particular technological development were becoming all too obvious. Early equipment was wearing out and diversity was making maintenance more problematical than it need be. Consequently, in 1877 it was agreed to follow LNWR practice in mechanical signalling matters and adopt that company's lever frame design as a new standard. The following year manufacture commenced at the NL's Bow Works.

This arrangement lasted only a few years, and by the end of the 1880s the NL was manufacturing frames of its own design. The most noteworthy element of the new design was the use of tappet locking, the NL being amongst the first to adopt this following the expiry of Stevens & Sons' original 1870 patent. Interestingly, a distinctive feature carried over from LNWR frames was the use of loop handles in front of the levers.

4. Signalbox Design

Despite the fact that the NL was in the forefront of absolute block working and interlocking, almost no illustrations of the company's first signalboxes survive. They would undoubtedly have been small structures with no architectural pretensions. McKenzie & Holland signalboxes are known to have been provided when that firm undertook resignalling contracts in the 1870s, but the majority of boxes from that decade that did survive to be analysed were obviously built to railway company designs. The hipped roof was the only feature the various structures had in common.

The type of signalboxes erected after 1878 indicated that a standard design had finally been created. These new structures, classified by the Signalling Study Group as Type 2, also had hipped roofs, small operating room window sash units just two panes wide and two panes deep, and vertical boarding both above and below these windows. The succeeding version of this design with a gabled roof (Type 3a) was also built with large removable locking room windows to give access to new frames with tappet locking. The NL's final designs varied only in the distribution of glazing bars in the operating room windows. In 1909 the LNWR took control of the company, retiring Pryce from his position as Signal Superintendent and sourcing all future signalling requirements from Crewe.

LONDON, MIDLAND & SCOTTISH RAILWAY

Surprisingly, considering its conservative approach to signalling, it was the ex-MR signalling works at Derby which turned out the first standard upper quadrant semaphores to be used on the new LMS. Many of these, and the subsequent variants described in the Introduction, were fitted to existing pre-Grouping posts. The LMS did continue to erect new timber as well as metal lattice posts in its early years, but during the 1930s it started to erect tubular steel posts in line with the LNER and GWR. This practice was, of course, continued by BR after nationalisation. For junction or cantilevered signals, metal lattice posts with ex-LNWR pattern brackets were preferred until the late 1930s when first tubular posts and then simpler steel channel fabrications either bolted or welded together were used instead.

The first colour-light signals were brought into use in June 1929 at Manchester on the western approaches to Exchange and Victoria stations. These were multi-aspect signals, the majority arranged as 'clusters' (as described in the Southern Railway chapter). Two new signalboxes and a large ground frame were provided to control the new layout, each equipped with Westinghouse Style 'K' frames of miniature levers and mechanical tappet interlocking.

The most significant installation of colour-light signals, however, was brought into use in 1932 on the 2¾-mile stretch of line between Heaton Lodge Junction and Thornhill LNWR Junction, Mirfield. The type of colour-light signals used were not multi-aspect but of the searchlight design, the difference being that the former displayed only one colour per lens, whereas the latter was capable of displaying three colours per lens because each unit incorporated a movable spectacle containing different coloured glasses which could be moved in front of the bulb. Searchlight signals were used in this particular

Above:
A good example of an LMS 'conspicuous' metal lattice post with LNWR-type fabricated bracket supporting a pair of steel channels forming the 'trimmer' (the cantilevered extension), and a tubular steel doll. Both arms had a variant of the twin glass standard spectacle with what appeared to be (but was not) a space for a third glass. *J. A. Peden*

Above:
The impressive LMR Standard frame in Carlisle No 5 signalbox, opened in September 1951. The levers were spaced at 4½in and, as in many frames of this pattern, the lever tops were covered with white plastic (see also cover illustration).
BR(LMR) official photograph

installation because A. F. Bound wanted to experiment with 'speed signalling', pioneered in North America, which required a number of different combinations of light to be displayed. It is not appropriate to explain the workings here; sufficient to record that the principle was not taken up by any other signal engineer.

Whereas the LMS used off-the-shelf upper quadrant and colour-light signals, it did not share a standard design of signalbox with any of the other 'Big Four' companies. In the end, it was the ex-MR pattern, more or less in its final form, which became the company's standard for England and Wales. There were detail differences, but apart from those structures given LNWR-style brick bases, the 'new' signalbox design was unmistakably an MR product. For signalboxes north of the border, a completely new design was used. This had a brick base, hipped and slate-covered roof and tall operating room window units divided into four by heavy glazing bars, the two upper panes of glass being a third the size of the lower pair. The most prominent feature, however, was a cantilevered bay formed from the central four-pane window unit.

Just before the outbreak of World War 2 the LMS produced a signalbox design intended to withstand bomb blasts. The other 'Big Four' companies also erected what became known generically as ARP (Air Raid Precaution) signalboxes. The LMS design had 14in-thick brick walls, and a roof and operating room floor made up of Evanstone hollow reinforced concrete beams (named after the firm that manufactured them) covered with a concrete skim. The operating room windows were standard factory-made steel products which found their way into more than just railway structures. Surprisingly, the finished signalboxes were handsome buildings, the concrete surround to the windows and the double string-course of different coloured bricks, sometimes laid on end,

Above:
Beeston South Junction, just outside Nottingham, was one of the all-timber LMS standard signalboxes built between 1929 and 1933 in England and Wales. It was classified LMS Type 11b by the Signalling Study Group in the 1970s. Each timber section (or 'flake') was 10ft wide. *R. S. Carpenter collection*

preventing the structures from looking too austere.

When it came to equipment inside the signalbox, the LMS never introduced a standard block instrument, preferring to maintain and modify with a variety of block controls existing pre-Grouping equipment. It did, however, manage to design a new standard mechanical lever frame for use in England and Wales based entirely on the last MR pattern. The most noticeable difference between the new LMS and the old MR frames was the spacing of the levers — 4½in instead of 6in. There were other differences such as the baseplate castings made to support groups of five rather than four levers, but overall the parentage of the frame was never in doubt. The design was also championed by the Railway Executive Committee (REC) who hoped to make it the standard frame for all the country's railways. Naturally, as Britons have always been suspicious of conformity, and companies such as the GWR would probably have never been persuaded, this recommendation was never implemented.

Nevertheless, further modifications were made to this 'REC' frame in 1943 to create the LMR Standard frame which continued to be manufactured at Crewe until the very end of the 1960s. Two variants were produced, one with levers spaced at 4½in as before, but another with a gap of 6in between levers so that the replacement of worn out ex-MR frames could be made without going to the additional expense of altering the 'lead-offs' from the signalbox (for signal wires and pulleys, point rodding cranks, etc). In Scotland neither the REC nor the LMR Standard designs were used, but standardisation was achieved by using the Stevens/Caledonian pattern frame for 'new' and replacement work. These frames, eventually made up of second-hand parts, continued to be fitted into signalboxes north of the border into the 1970s.

Left:
Kilmacolm signalbox on the ex-G&SWR line west of Glasgow was an example of the LMS standard design used in Scotland, classified by the Signalling Study Group as LMS Type 12. *R. E. Ruffell*

Below:
The final development in mechanical signalbox design was the BR(LMR) Type 15. It appeared following a short period (1948-54) when the new BR(LMR) Architects' Department had been responsible for a number of different brick-based signalboxes. The Type 15 was designed by W. F. Hardman of the Signal Department, and its prefabricated timber panels could be built either on a brick or timber base. Macclesfield box opened in 1965, replacing the LMS standard Type 11b seen on the left. *M. S. Welch*

2
The London & North Eastern Railway

Apart from the GWR, which continued largely unaltered as an organisation up to 1948, the LNER probably had fewer problems in almost all facets of its operation than any of the other 'Big Four' companies as a result of the Grouping. The new company was divided into three Areas — Southern, North Eastern and Scottish — with the various Signal & Telegraph Engineers responsible to each Area's Engineers Department. There was much synergy already between the pre-1923 companies absorbed into those areas. In the North Eastern Area only the former Hull & Barnsley Railway had to be subdued into what was in effect the 'Greater NER'. In the Southern Area, the amalgamation of the GNR, GER and GCR had already been mooted back in 1908. In Scotland, only the Great North of Scotland Railway (GNSR) seemed a strange bed-fellow, isolated as it was from the other natural East Coast partner, the North British Railway (NBR).

With the exception of the GER, block working was based on three-position, three-wire block instruments and bells for double lines, and Tyer's Electric Train Tablet system for single lines. The former GER was equipped with Tyer's one-wire, two-position 'flap' block instruments with Sykes 'Lock & Block' in the London area. On the Southern Area there were examples of all the main signalling contractors' lever frame designs, which the former GER works at Leyton was charged with maintaining and periodically replacing. McKenzie & Holland pattern frames became the natural standard in the North Eastern Area, serviced from York, and Stevens' tappet pattern already predominated in Scotland. There was, of course, a huge variety of lower quadrant semaphores, but when the decision was made to replace these progressively with upper quadrants of a standard design this seems to have been a painless if protracted exercise over the whole network.

What distinguished the LNER from the other Grouping companies, however, was not maintenance of the status quo, but the progressive approach it took to developing new signalling equipment and practices. This was almost entirely due to the vision and drive of A. E. Tattersall, Signal Engineer of the North Eastern Area between 1928 and 1943. His achievements are recorded at the end of this chapter.

NORTH EASTERN RAILWAY

1. Signals

It is recorded that the Stockton & Darlington Railway (S&D) originally used fire baskets and torches to control the movement of trains at night. Fifteen years after it opened, a more sophisticated type of fixed signal was to be found at eight places along the line including the junction of the Croft Branch. For use during the day an unremarkable rectangular board on top of a post could be rotated to give a danger or caution indication. The real novelty of the signal, however, was the very large and unique style of lamp for use at night. Designed by Thomas Summerson and W. Russel, it had two rectangular coloured glasses, a red on top of a green. A shutter could be placed in front of these glasses before the whole lamp was hoisted to the top of the post. If the green was obscured and only the red light could be seen, this obviously told a driver to stop. If, however, both green and red lights were visible, this indicated caution. Presumably, no light meant the line was clear.

During the 1850s, simpler lamps were used as well as circular discs, and the S&D also started to erect auxiliary, or wire, signals so that trains could be stopped before they entered stations. These signals took the form of the top half of a rectangular board which had been cut across the diagonal. In the early years of the following decade, Bouch, the Locomotive Engineer, developed what was later christened a 'butterfly' signal, which was used on the Central Division of the NER. This, too, was a board signal with the lamp mounted on top, but with the ability to give both a positive danger and all-clear indication when the lamp was not lit. Four rectangular boards were fixed to a central vertical rod which passed through a hollow iron post. Each board was set at 90° to its neighbour so that in plan view the boards formed a cross. Two adjacent boards were painted red for danger, and when they were

Above:
This NER miniature semaphore ground signal at Tweedmouth clearly shows the way the arm was slotted into the wooden post. On this particular signal, the drive rod was attached to the cast-iron spectacle fitted on to the pivot of the arm. On full-size signals the rod was connected to a strap attached to the back of the arm. *A. G. Ellis*

rotated through 90° the other two boards painted white for all-clear became visible. In everyday use the signal proved inefficient and was soon replaced by the ubiquitous three-position lower quadrant, slot-in-the-post semaphore.

Board signals remained in use on the NER into the early 1870s, often used as distant signals at stations protected by double arm semaphores. (Amazingly, examples remained in use at level crossings into the 1960s.) It was, however, the two-position lower quadrant signal with its arm pivoted in a slot in the post which, from the 1870s to the Grouping (and beyond), became the most memorable feature of NER signalling. When other railway companies gradually abandoned this type of semaphore from the end of the 1870s because it had proved to be the main cause of the Abbotts Ripton disaster on the GNR in 1876, the NER remained faithful to the design. Even when the NER entered the power signalling age in the first decade of the 20th century, installing some of the most modern control equipment in the country, the electro-pneumatic 'motors' were still connected to slot-in-the-post semaphores.

Undoubtedly, one of the most compelling reasons originally for perpetuating this style of signal was that large numbers were already in use by the end of the 1870s, and the NER was a large network. But by 1923 that early tally must have appeared insignificant compared to the hundreds of new slot-in-the-post signals erected in the interim, for the railway company was lavish in its provision of semaphores for all manner of traffic movements. Not surprisingly, because of the extended use of these old-fashioned semaphores, the NER achieved an enviable conformity in design compared with other railways. The only significant design modification during the life of these signals occurred after the white light was abandoned as the all-clear indication in the 1890s. The single circular red glass spectacle was then substituted for one with two beehive-shaped glasses — red for danger and green for all-clear.

By the beginning of the 20th century, not only was there invariably a forest of signals at NER junctions and major stations but the company also used substantial gantries and brackets to support these semaphores, which were some of the most robust structures to be found on any British railway. McKenzie & Holland's solidly engineered cast-iron plate brackets and its wrought-iron lattice fabrications could be found all over the system. In the Southern Division, as with the individual signal posts, almost all the dolls were timber, but on the Northern Division, metal lattice was also preferred for dolls and posts.

2. Signalling Equipment, Electrical

The only company other than the SER to use Walker's semaphore block instruments was the NER on ex-S&D lines. Everywhere else on the system was eventually equipped with standard three-position needle instruments and block bells for controlling absolute and permissive block sections. As with its use of an outdated semaphore, the NER also perpetuated the use of old block instruments.

Above:
A pair of typical McKenzie & Holland bracket signals at York with crude finials. Behind 'A1' No 2581 *Neil Gow*, Waterworks signalbox can be seen with its angled corners, awning and decorative balcony railings, one of a number of signalboxes of this special design opened at the new York station in 1877.
Author's collection

Double-needle instruments of the type employed by the LNWR in the 1850s remained in use long after other companies had replaced theirs. A photograph of the interior of Hull Paragon station signalbox, with its 1904 electro-pneumatic frame, shows very clearly two of these instruments. The peg-and-chain arrangement for maintaining the drop handles in position on these and their single-needle equivalents (described on page 13) survived until the Grouping. It was not until LNER ownership that single-needle pegging instruments were modified with a rotary three-position commutator, as fitted to the latest standard Tyer & Co block instrument.

Either very late in the NER's independent existence, or early in LNER days, a new double-needle instrument was developed, very obviously based on the existing single-needle design. This was originally fitted with a circular commutator handle very similar to that fitted to some Tyer & Co's and Fletcher's standard LNWR instruments. This handle was also replaced in time with the rotary version mentioned above. For permissive block working, the NER made use of Tyer & Co's single-needle instruments, and at York (and probably a few other locations), Sykes' lever and treadle locks were installed.

3. Signalling Equipment, Mechanical

By the end of the 1850s, the NER was bringing together, or 'concentrating' as it was known then, the mechanisms for working signals and points at junctions, but the company did not have any interlocking between the levers at such locations until the following decade. The first reference to new interlocking apparatus on the NER was made in September 1862, when five sets were ordered from John Saxby. Another five years elapsed before interlocking work began in earnest, first at junctions, and then spreading progressively to stations in the 1870s. This approach was very similar to that taken by the NER's East Coast partner, the GNR.

Above:
The interior of Alnmouth signalbox on 13 September 1952, showing the very pronounced angle levers in McKenzie & Holland frames assumed when pulled towards the signalmen. Notice how the supports for the block shelf were substantial cast-iron brackets bolted to the quadrant plates of the frame. Just visible on the shelf are two 'combined' NER/LNER block instruments. *R. K. Blencowe collection*

As with the GNR, the majority of mechanical signalling equipment was acquired from signalling contractors who also installed their own products. Each operational district or division of the NER — Northern, Central and Southern — had its own favourite contractor, although none ever had a complete monopoly of jobs on offer. After employing Saxby & Farmer, Easterbrook & Co, I'Anson & Sons, Tweedy and Stevens & Sons in the 1870s, most Northern Division signalling eventually went to the last-named, that firm's tappet frames becoming more common than any other. The Central Division (until it was disbanded and absorbed into the other districts in 1899) also favoured that firm, but, by contrast, the Northern Division's bias towards McKenzie & Holland evolved into a single-supplier agreement at the beginning of the 20th century. After installing many examples of at least four of its patent frame designs, in 1903 McKenzie & Holland launched its Pattern Nos 16 and 17 which immediately became the standard mechanical frames on this division. The only difference between the two patterns was the spacing (pitch) between the levers — 5in in the case of No 16 and 4in for pattern No 17. The largest ever frame of levers in one continuous row — 295 — was of Pattern Nos 16/17 installed in Locomotive Yard signalbox, York, in 1909. Manufacture of Nos 16/17 Pattern by the Westinghouse Brake & Signal Co, Tyer & Co, The Railway Signal Co and Henry Williams continued after the Grouping and in 1925 it became the standard frame of the North Eastern Area of the LNER. Examples made up of second parts were still being installed after the nationalisation of Britain's railways in 1948, the very last ones appearing at the end of the 1960s.

The NER may have boasted the largest mechanical lever frame, but in the same decade as this came into use it was also committed to a number of progressive power signalling schemes. In 1902 McKenzie & Holland was employed to equip Tyne Docks Coal Yard with Westinghouse electro-pneumatic apparatus, the signalling contractor having secured the British licence for this in 1895. Following the success of that installation, the NER commissioned a larger one at Hull Paragon station in 1904. Two signalboxes were fitted with Westinghouse's latest miniature lever frame, the Style 'B', introduced only the previous year. Although the frames and pneumatic equipment were

This page:
A typical slot-in-the-post semaphore with lattice post and distinctive McKenzie & Holland finial but operated by a pneumatic 'motor' visible immediately below the arm. This was part of the NER's first electro-pneumatic installation provided by the Worcester firm at Tyne Docks, Green Lane signalbox in the background containing a frame of miniature levers. *M. Dunnett*

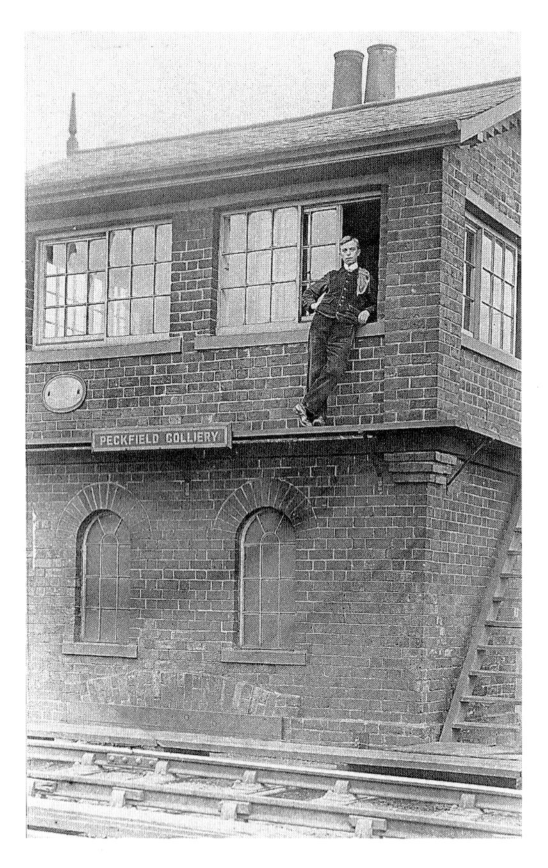

Above:
In the first decade of the 20th century a confident young signalman stands in charge of the NER's Type S1a signalbox at Peckfield Colliery. The brick coursing chosen by the builder of this structure was Flemish bond. *J. M. Ryan collection*

of a brand-new design, the semaphores and other mechanical fittings were all standard NER patterns.

The initial cost of any power signalling scheme was considerably higher than that for a more conventional mechanical installation, and the NER's main reason for adopting the former seems to have been based on whether or not there was space for a traditional signalbox. At York the company obviously felt there was enough room for a huge new 295 mechanical lever frame, but at Newcastle even with miniature lever frames, three out of the total of eight signal cabins needed to control the complex layout had to be erected over the tracks. The largest of these was Newcastle No 1 with 198 miniature levers, although the conventional brick-based Newcastle No 3 actually housed the most miniature levers of the whole scheme — 211. Interestingly, the Newcastle scheme was completed in the same year (1909) that Locomotive Yard, York, was brought into use.

4. Signalbox Design

There appear to be almost no images of pre-1870 signalling huts, towers or stages on the NER. What structures there may have been were almost certainly not built to a standard design. As with nearly every railway company in this country, the 1870s witnessed a spate of signalbox building on the NER when the first obviously standardised designs began to appear.

Signalboxes on the Northern Division changed very little over the years. The majority were built of brick and had hipped, slate-covered roofs. Operating room sash window units were either two or three panes in height by two panes wide. The panes were invariably tall and narrow. The only way the Signalling Study Group found of usefully classifying the styles was by comparing the windows in the locking rooms. Between 1870 and the 1890s single windows were used, often simple domestic sash windows with standard vertical sliding units. For a few years spanning the turn of the century the single window was joined by two smaller ones either side, all three units sharing the same stone lintel and sill. Then from about 1905 until the Grouping a single larger window with an elliptical top and brick lintel replaced this arrangement.

The most distinctive signalboxes built on the Northern Division were those which straddled the tracks on massive iron gantries and brackets, supported by either substantial metal posts or brick piers. As mentioned above, when Newcastle station was resignalled between 1905 and 1909 a number of overhead cabins were built and equipped with frames of miniature levers for working the electro-pneumatic signalling equipment.

On the Central Division, signalboxes built from the beginning of the 1870s and into the 1880s were brick structures with steeply pitched gabled roofs, the masonry extending to the apex of the roof. The most noticeable feature was the extended finial connected by crossed timbers to the barge boards on each pitch of the roof. The sash units in the operating room windows were arranged in groups of three, each unit being two panes wide by three panes high. Later structures built at the turn of the century were provided with hipped roofs, one particular variant including a triangular vent at the apex of the roof, forming, in effect, a small vertical gable.

Above:
An example at Fighting Cocks of the NER's first standard signalbox design used on its Central Division in the 1870s and '80s (Type C1), photographed from a passing train in September 1963.
Real Photographs/Ian Allan Library

The first standard all-brick signalboxes of the Southern Division were reminiscent of early LSWR, GWR and Bristol & Exeter Railway structures, with the operating room windows let into the masonry. All had gabled roofs and prominent brick corner pillars, corbelled out from the main walls from operating room floor level up to the eaves and then continued on the gable ends as a feature up to the apex of the roof. This made the operating room windows appear to be recessed, although they were in fact fitted flush with the main wall line. The locking room windows were invariably tall and narrow with semi-circular heads.

Structures of this style, classified Type S1 by the Signalling Study Group, were built until 1903, when they were superseded by what might be termed more conventional signalboxes, the operating room window sash units being arranged in a continuous row along the front. Considering how standard the early design had been, and for how long, there were a number of variations on the later design. Some boxes had no barge boards, whilst others were fitted with examples having a distinct upturn at the eaves level. Some had the same locking room windows as the previous type, whilst others had rectangular ones. The most noticeable variant appeared on the York to Burton Salmon widening scheme, where the signalboxes were built with generous top lights above the main operating room windows. These structures could not have contrasted more with their predecessors in terms of the amount of glazing provided.

The final design built from 1905 up to and beyond the Grouping was based on the Type S2 and S3 boxes just described with gables roofs covered with slates. The operating room sash window units in these new structures were even larger, four panes high by either six or eight panes wide, the opening sashes at either end of the front elevation being exactly half the width (ie three or four panes wide). The largest Type S4 was, of course, Locomotive Yard signalbox at York, opened in 1909, a massive brick-based structure almost 150ft long.

GREAT EASTERN RAILWAY

1. Signals

One of the earliest surviving rule books is from the Eastern Counties Railway (ECR). Issued in 1846, it mentions, amongst other things, three-position lower quadrant station semaphores. By the time the new 1857 Rules & Regulations Book appeared, auxiliary signals were also being described. According to the rule book these signals were positioned 600yd away from the station signal and worked to only two positions — all-clear and danger. At both stations and junctions Rules 43 and 79 stated that the normal position of auxiliaries was 'all-clear'. Rule 38 instructed that 'immediately an Engine or Train has passed one of these Signals, it must be placed at Danger; but should a Train arrive before the Line is clear, it must be brought to a stand outside the Auxiliary Signal, which must be lowered to allow the Train to pass within it for protection, when the Danger Signal must again be exhibited'. These auxiliary signals, of course, eventually evolved into distant signals and were worked in a very different way under block working regulations.

The design of GER semaphores developed in a similar fashion to those used by other railway companies. Originally the three-position lower quadrant arm was pivoted in a slot in the main post, with the spectacle at the base of that slot. As absolute block working was refined in the early 1870s, the arm of both stop and distant signals was arranged to work to only two positions — danger and all-clear. By the end of that decade new signals were being erected with the arm pivoted on the front face of the post. At the end of the arm surrounding the pivot was a cast circular plate whose diameter was the same as the width of the arm. As with LBSCR semaphore arms, GER examples tapered towards the pivot end. During the 1890s the next development was the attaching of the twin glass spectacle to this plate. Betraying their ancestry until the end, the pivot plate and the spectacle were never redesigned as one casting.

2. Signalling Equipment, Electrical

One of the earliest lines which later became part of the GER was that opened between Minories and Blackwall, London, in 1840. Not only was its 5ft gauge of note but so was its method of transporting passengers to and from the intermediate stations. Individual carriages were attached and detached from a continuous cable, and to control this system an elaborate version of Cooke & Wheatstone's electric telegraph was installed. Each station had a single-needle telegraph instrument, on which the centrally pivoted vertical needle could be deflected one way to indicate 'ready' and the opposite way to indicate 'stop'. At the terminal stations all the intermediate station's indications were repeated on a combined instrument. An electrical bell was used to 'call attention' of the winding drum brakesmen and enginemen, and by deflecting the needle to the appropriate indication, the necessary action could be taken. This was the first time the electric telegraph had been used to control the movement of trains.

Another constituent of the GER, the Norfolk Railway, was also in the forefront of using the electric telegraph to regulate trains. When it opened its single track line between Norwich and Yarmouth in 1844, the stations were equipped with Cooke & Wheatstone instruments from the start. The electric telegraph eventually found its way along all the GER's routes, but what had once been the wonder of the age in the 1840s began to prove inadequate for the management of increasing traffic two decades later. The very shaky financial position of the new GER formed in 1862 meant no progress was made with block working in that decade, and it was not until receipts increased at the beginning of the 1870s and pressure was exerted by the Board of Trade that improvements were made.

To extend absolute block working as economically as possible the GER, not surprisingly, was convinced by Edward Tyer's arguments for one-wire block telegraph instruments. The railway company chose to adopt his two-position, twin-needle variety with separate block bell and plunger, two sets of this combination being needed in each signalbox controlling a stretch of double track. By 1876 Tyer & Co was supplying its needle and miniature semaphore instruments with a screen or 'flap' which acted as a reminder to the signalman as to which plunger he needed to operate. Whether the GER used instruments with this arrangement as early as the mid-1870s is not known, but certainly by the Grouping they all had them. As the Tyer's instruments used by the GER had the plungers aligned horizontally, the flap was pivoted vertically. To operate the Line Clear plunger, the flap had to be moved to the left to cover the Train on Line plunger and then the flap's green side was visible. When the flap was moved to the right so that its black side was visible it then covered the Train on Line plunger.

Above:
The impressive arrangement of standard GER semaphores at Cromer (High) in 1951. The finials indicate McKenzie & Holland was responsible for the work but also of note is the 'bow-tie' calling-on arm, the full-size goods line arm with ring and the very small arms at the base of the posts repeating the indications of just the three main arms. *W. S. Garth*

Above:
A close-up of the standard GER lower quadrant distant signal semaphore with twin glass cast-iron spectacle at Beccles Swing Bridge. Photographed on 6 September 1952. *R. E. Vincent*

When three-position block working came into force in the 1890s, an additional 'mini-flap' was attached to the existing device, and cleverly arranged so that it could display Train Passed or Train on Line. The movement of the flaps, however, was not connected in any way with the electrical circuitry of the instrument, and in many respects they were merely a cosmetic arrangement, a mechanical reminder for the signalman. The operation of the switch hook on Sykes 'Lock & Block' instruments, by comparison, did not act just as a reminder, it had an electrical function as well. The GER's 'flap blocks', as they became known by later enthusiasts, were a good example of a once-state-of-the-art piece of technology given an artificially extended life by crude mechanical additions.

Mentioning Sykes 'Lock & Block' is appropriate here, because the GER installed the most sophisticated variant of his 1880 patent apparatus on its busy London lines in 1896. The GER instruments were capable of displaying an additional indication — TRAIN ACCEPTED — as well as TRAIN ON. To reduce the temptation for a signalman to misuse the release key to 'unlock' the system, co-operation was needed by adjacent signalmen. The signalman sending the train had to press a button which electrically unlocked a shutter across the release keyhole in the instrument in the signalbox awaiting the train. Whilst the shutter was open and the key in the instrument, the circuit between the two signalboxes was broken, removing any risk of the signalman leaving the release key permanently in the instrument. If the lever controlling the signal allowing a train into a forward section had to be unlocked in special circumstances, other than in the normal sequence of events, then the signalman in advance (ie who would be receiving any train passed by the signal concerned) had to press a button to electrically release the 'back-lock' on that signal lever. Co-operation in this way reduced the risk of abuse.

On all Britain's railways until the very end of the 19th century, a lever in a signalbox was able to operate a signal or point because there was a continuous mechanical connection between the two. The mechanical movement of the lever was transferred along wires, chains, cranks and rods to the piece of lineside equipment. Expansion and contraction of all this metalwork had to be taken into account when making the connections, which meant compensators of various designs had to be built into long runs of wire or rodding. Large installations meant large quantities of ironmongery by the trackside, increasing maintenance and presenting a potential hazard to staff.

The obvious solution was to place the power source to operate the lineside equipment next to that equipment and the GER was the first company in this country to achieve this when in January 1899 it brought into use an electro-pneumatic system at Spitalfields goods station. Inside Whitechapel signalbox (usually referred to by its later name, Granary Junction) the company fitted an American 'table interlocker'. This was the equivalent of the lever frame, but, as its name implies, it was more like a large table with handles arranged along the front. When a handle was turned to its first intermediate position, an electrical current passed to the electro-magnet of a hydraulic cylinder placed next to the signal or point to be operated. The current opened the valve to allow air into the cylinder to move the piece of equipment. Once this had been achieved, a return current pushed the handle to its fully 'reversed' position. If for any reason the signal or point did not respond correctly (ie could not be 'proved'), no reverse current flowed, the handle remained in its intermediate position and the interlocking in the frame was not freed for any conflicting handles to be operated. This principle applied to all subsequent 'power signalling' installations. What was also possible with this and most subsequent power signalling installations was the selection of signals depending on the position of points. This meant one handle

Above:
Part of the Saxby & Farmer 1888 Duplex pattern frame (patent 1888, No 183) in the GER signalbox at Cavendish, photographed on 4 February 1967. This type of frame was the first by this firm to incorporate tappet locking originally patented by Stevens & Sons in 1870 (No 746). On the Duplex frame there were two tappet irons connected to each lever, one driven by the catch-handle and activating the locking, the other driven by the movement of the lever imparting extra travel to its partner. In other words, a typical example of clever Victorian design. *P. Hocquard*

could control a number of different signals, the lie of the points 'selecting' which signal responded to the handle.

3. Signalling Equipment, Mechanical

Saxby & Farmer was the first to provide the ECR with interlocking equipment in 1861. As far as is know, this firm fulfilled all the company's requirements from then until the early years of the following decade. In 1870 Stevens & Sons secured its first contract, and the following year Saxby & Farmer tried to negotiate a sole agreement with the GER but failed. With a growing number of signalling contractors anxious to enter a lucrative market, the GER was happy to approach others including Ransomes & Rapier, McKenzie & Holland, The Railway Signal Co, Dutton & Co and, much later (1897-1901), Evans O'Donnell.

Interestingly, between 1876 and 1885, the GER awarded annual agreements to the signalling contractor who submitted the lowest prices. After this the company worked out the cost of individual jobs and who to employ by referring to lists of prices supplied by all its main contractors.

As a result of first competitive tendering and then annual agreements, the GER acquired over the years a variety of lever frame designs. There were examples of many different Saxby & Farmer frames: the July 1867 Patent (No 2119), the 1871 Patent Rocker (No 1601), and its successor and far more numerous 1874 Patent Rocker & Gridiron (No 294), the 1888 Duplex (patent 1888, No 183) and its successor the 1905 Duplex (not patented), which the signalling contractor supplied almost exclusively to the GER. McKenzie & Holland provided whatever its current lever frame design was: there were Stevens tappet frames patented in 1870 (No 746), and examples of Dutton's patent of 1893 (No 1343), Evans O'Donnell's frames and, of course, The Railway Signal Co's tappet design manufactured from 1884. It was perhaps fortunate that, when the GER was absorbed into the LNER, the GNR was also part of that new company, for it too had the same variety of lever frames and, more importantly, the same useful stock of spare parts.

4. Signalbox Design

Almost inevitably, the first recognisable signalbox on the ECR was erected and fitted out by Saxby & Farmer. This was located at the busy Stratford junction just east of London and was opened in 1861. Other junctions were subsequently protected with Saxby's equipment, so that by the beginning of the 1870s there were a number of fully interlocked Saxby & Farmer signalboxes on the GER. When the GER started to employ other contractors, their signalbox designs also began to appear.

Concurrently, signalling contractors were also erecting signalboxes of the railway company's own design, with detail differences depending on who built the structures. What all signalboxes had in common were shallow hipped roofs and a box-frame timber superstructure divided into square panels. The window sashes were fitted into the panels in the upper half of the frame, whilst the lower panels were

Above:
A lovely example of one of the first GER Type 1 signalboxes, in this instance built in the 1870s by McKenzie & Holland of Worcester. This particular example at Chesterton Junction, photographed in the first decade of the 20th century, had a brick base built around the timber frame. *Ian Allan Library*

filled with boarding. This was aligned either horizontally or vertically except in the corner panels where it was inclined at an angle of 45°. The locking room bases were also timber framed with boarded panels, sometimes with the diagonal cross-bracing visible on the exterior (as with certain Furness Railway signalboxes).

The hipped roof was abandoned in the mid-1870s, and what became the GER Type 2 signalbox began to appear about 1878. Most of these were once again of all-timber construction, the overhanging roofs finished with either plain or notched barge boards, slightly larger operating room windows than previously and panels of horizontal weatherboarding. It was this style of signalbox that was used on the new stretches of the GN&GEJt line when that opened in 1882 and which the GNR subsequently used for a number of years on its own lines.

After 1882 GER signalboxes all had a strong family resemblance but varied in details. The majority of signalboxes constructed by McKenzie & Holland in 1882/3, for example, had operating room sash units with one central large pane of glass sandwiched between two smaller panes above and below, and two tall narrow panes to the left and right (see p76). The windows of a number of signalboxes built by Saxby & Farmer for the GER between 1884 and 1889 had the top three panels of each sash unit divided into four smaller panes. These Type 5/S&F boxes also had decorative panels in the gable ends and unusual barge boards connected along the bottom edge of the roof by an ornate awning. Structures erected by McKenzie & Holland in 1885/6 also had an awning, the style of which was carried up the top section of the gable end barge boards. The way the GER allocated its signalling contracts annually may have had something to do with this amount of unnecessary decoration, each contractor trying to outdo its rival.

From the mid-1880s decoration was curtailed and most signalboxes built between then and the Grouping had plain barge boards. Nevertheless, each contractor managed to modify the basic design in some small way, Dutton & Co, for example, providing its structures with substantial porches covered by an extension of the main roof.

NORTH BRITISH RAILWAY

1. Signals

The Edinburgh & Glasgow Railway (E&G) rule book of January 1842 is one of this author's favourites, simply because of its explanation of the use of the green caution signal, '. . . exhibited by the Police, or workmen on the line'. During the day a green flag was used, and at night a lamp showing a green light, and on seeing this signal a driver was to expect '. . . some important information . . . for his guidance . . . [and to] prepare for receiving such communication by reducing speed to such as a man can easily run alongside and speak to him; but the Engineman is not to stop the Train on account of the green signal.'

Above:
The base of one of the stop signals on the NBR's Lennoxtown branch. The lamp is shown in its lowered position, attached to a cradle which could be winched up and down the side of the metal lattice post. The winch handle would have been fitted to the projecting bar immediately beneath the counter balance. *A. G. Ellis*

Before long, fixed signals in the form of revolving boards began to be installed at stations and when these were superseded by standard three-position slot-in-the-post semaphores, they were relegated to serve as distant/auxiliary signals. The final form of some of these 'vane' signals was very ornate and they were often mounted on decorative cast-iron pillars. Each area of the NBR had its own shaped boards, but all were pivoted centrally with a lamp mounted above them on the end of the central spindle. Those on the Monkland section were almost identical to the boards used by the CR on its Southern Division — a pierced oval plate with a small rectangular extension — whilst on the Stirling and Dunfermline section they were long pierced cross-bars. On the Edinburgh & Glasgow line the signals had three very decorative vanes arranged, in plan, as a 'T'. This configuration was identical to that of the G&SWR's three-disc signal, but unlike that signal which was used to give only two indications, the NBR pattern was used to display a positive danger, caution or all-clear indication. In this respect it was unique.

As with most Scottish railways, by the end of the 1860s the majority of NBR signalling equipment was being supplied by Stevens & Sons. Semaphores were mounted on metal lattice posts capped with cast pierced ball and spike finials, and where bracket signals were needed, simple straps supported the offset landing and post (doll). Signal spectacles had Stevens distinctive 'grape-shaped' glasses, and many posts had windlass equipment so that lamps could be winched into position behind the spectacle from ground level.

2. Signalling Equipment, Electrical

For controlling train movements over the inconvenient cable-operated incline between its Queen Street terminus in Glasgow and Cowlairs, opened in 1842, the E&G installed Cooke & Wheatstone electric telegraph equipment using 15 different coded messages. When Tyer & Co published the fifth edition of its catalogue in 1874, it included the NBR in the list of its customers, although it did not state which type of instruments the company used.

Eventually, the NBR settled on standard three-wire, three-position block instruments and bells for its double-track lines. Electrically these were identical to those used by the NER, GNR and MR, to name but a few other users, but two features are worthy of note. The majority of these type of instruments were fitted with C. E. Spagnoletti's patent single-needle units, but those used by the NBR were fitted with an earlier design. In Spagnoletti's pattern the needle on the front of the dial was a brass strip attached to an armature with two iron fins which pivoted between the electro-magnets behind the dial. On NBR instruments, the indicating needle was of iron, which was attracted to the two electro-magnets, the ends of which protruded through the face of the dial either side of the needle. The NBR was not the only user of these types of needles (the CR used them, for example), but it is, perhaps, more associated with this particular pattern than any other railway company. The second feature was also not unique to NBR instruments but it was shared with only one other railway company, the GCR in England. To supersede the peg-and-chain arrangement on its pegging instruments, the NBR adopted the same thumb catch device as fitted to GCR equipment. As well as new instruments, old ones were also refurbished with the new catch.

There were also other examples of the NBR using variants of otherwise standard equipment, but on a small scale. The Sykes Interlocking Co supplied a special form of its 'Lock & Block' instrument with a three-position single-needle unit in place of the top miniature semaphore indicator, and with a drop handle immediately beneath the brass plunger.

In 1915/16 the railway company chose the Sykes Non Token Block system for working trains over the Lothian lines just outside Edinburgh. This was the equivalent of Sykes' 'Lock & Block' but for single lines and was unique until the introduction of BR's tokenless block system in the 1960s. Elsewhere, standard Tyer & Co's Electric Train Tablet system was used, and, from the last few years of the 19th century, when The Railway Signal Co began to manufacture Webb & Thompson's Electric Train Staff equipment, this was brought into use on a number of branches.

3. Signalling Equipment, Mechanical

The NBR remained third amongst Scottish railways in the Board of Trade's 'interlocking league table' throughout the last three decades of the 19th century. Interlocking was not completed at all locations until 1894. A few examples of Stevens' hook lever frame which made its first appearance in 1860 were installed, but the most common frames on the NBR were Stevens' Glasgow Old and New Pattern designs based on the firm's patent of 1870 (No 746), (see the Caledonian Railway section of the LMS chapter). The former was manufactured until the turn of the century, at which point the revised New Pattern superseded it.

The NBR did not rely totally on Stevens & Sons. The Railway Signal Co was awarded the contract to resignal Edinburgh Waverley station between 1892 and 1899, the East signalbox containing a frame of 260 levers, Waverley West a frame of 205 levers. For the West Highland lines opened from Craigendoran (west of Glasgow) to Fort William in 1894 and on to Mallaig in 1901, the NBR employed Saxby & Farmer for the first section and The Railway Signal Co for the final extension. Saxby & Farmer supplied its most recent frame design, the 1888 Duplex (patent 1888, No 183) incorporating tappet locking. This was Saxby & Farmer's first product not to have locking devised in-house. The Railway Signal Co, on the other hand, equipped the signalboxes on its contract with lever frames of Stevens & Sons pattern.

4. Signalbox Design

In the 1970s and '80s the Signalling Study Group managed to identify eight basic NBR signalbox designs, whilst admitting there was great variety within its classification. The evolution of what that Group designated Type 1 may have followed a similar course to that on the SER. Signalboxes built between the 1870s and the first few years of the 20th century shared two features in common with SER boxes — hipped roofs and operating room windows formed of standard domestic vertical sash windows. These were the only consistent features of the majority of NBR Type 1 signalboxes. They had brick bases which extended to the eaves on the rear and end elevations. An all-timber version with vertical flush tongue-and-groove boarding and another with a wooden superstructure on a brick base were classified by the Signalling Study Group as Type 3.

Type 2 signalboxes were apparently contemporary with Type 1 and Type 3 examples. Unlike those, however, the operating room windows were set individually within solid brick walls. On larger boxes vertical sash windows were inserted only at either end of the front elevation, the other windows being non-opening. The majority of structures built with this arrangement had hipped roofs and elliptical brick lintels above each window, but there were a few with semi-circular heads and gabled roofs.

The next recognisable category of NBR signalbox built in the last years of the Victorian era and the first of King Edward VII's reign was the last

Left:
The Stevens Glasgow New Pattern lever frame in Dunbar West signalbox. The block shelf supported standard three-wire block equipment, with detail difference preferred by the NBR, for example, the MS&LR/GCR-type thumb catch on the two visible pegging instruments. *Gilbert Ogilvie*

Right:
An example at Jedburgh of what the Signalling Study Group christened the NBR's Type 3 signalbox design. The vertical sash windows were a particular feature of NBR signalboxes built between the end of the 1870s and about 1908.
H. F. Wheeller/R. S. Carpenter collection

Above:
The two signalboxes at Edinburgh Waverley were built to a special design, obviously thought to be more appropriate for the NBR's major Scottish station. Opened when the station was enlarged between 1892 and 1899, the West box is shown here behind NBR 4-4-0 No 9281 departing for Glasgow a few years after the Grouping. *Author's collection*

to incorporate vertical sash windows. All windows could be opened, and whereas the previous types had only one vertical glazing bar, the windows of the new Type 4 had extra horizontal bars.

The signalboxes on the West Highland line (Type 6a) were reminiscent of CR Type 1 structures, with operating room windows made up of sash units three panes wide by three panes deep. For the Mallaig Extension, The Railway Signal Co modified its existing signalbox design by removing the additional row of sash units under the main operating room windows, and giving the structures hipped roofs with very prominent overhangs on all sides. The resultant signalboxes were particularly well proportioned.

From about 1908 the operating rooms of new NBR signalboxes were provided with generous areas of plate glass. Above these large sheets of glass in the same timber frame, smaller panes were inserted occupying about a third or quarter of the whole sash unit. Signalboxes erected after World War 1 had simple horizontal boarding substituted for this top glazing, and structures of this pattern continued to be built by the LNER until the middle of the 1930s.

GREAT NORTHERN RAILWAY

1. Signals

The GNR was one of the few railway companies to open with three-position, slot-in-the-post semaphores used as both station and auxiliary or distant signals. At stations and junctions, posts supported two arms for controlling trains travelling in opposite directions but, obviously, distant signals were fitted with only one arm.

The GNR bought much of its signalling equipment in the 1850s and '60s from Stevens & Sons who supplied a number of very tall metal lattice posts from 1860 onwards. In common with other railways, the GNR only lit its signal lamps at night, not only the lamps but the metal carrying cases being taken down during the day. To ease this process, Stevens' lamp lifting equipment was fitted to many signal posts. If the arm needed attention, however, the fitter was not so lucky, as the GNR preferred to fit many of its tall timber posts with cast-iron foot-holds rather than ladders.

With the spread of the block system in the 1870s and the building of dozens of new signalboxes, many more signals were erected. At stations twin-arm semaphores were replaced with separate posts and single arms for up and down directions, although posts carrying both up and down arms of post-1876 pattern lasted at some remote signalboxes until World War 1. Where signalboxes were close together, many home or starting signals of one box were simply slotted to act as the distant signal for the adjacent box, this practice surviving in some places until the beginning of the 1880s.

Until 1876, GNR semaphores were fundamentally no different from those of every other railway in the British Isles. What caused the GNR to be the first to redesign its signals completely in that year was the Abbotts Ripton accident. The story has been often repeated, and it is well known that what led to the pile-up of three trains at that remote spot was snow filling the slots and preventing the arms and the spectacles they were connected to being put to danger. Edward French, a signal fitter from Hitchin, must be credited with finding the solution. He designed an arm which was pivoted on a separate cast-iron bracket attached to the post. The pivot was equidistant from each end of the arm but just above its centreline, which meant that, if the rod operating it broke, the arm always pivoted to the horizontal danger position. A provisional patent was granted in 1877, and thereafter this new 'somersault' signal became the GNR's standard semaphore.

Above:
The GNR erected numerous very tall signal posts between the 1870s and first decade of the 20th century, after which they were not so popular. Ladders were provided to give lampmen access to the lamp and spectacle, but often, as shown here, the arm could only be reached using cast-iron foot-holds and an obvious degree of nerve. This arrangement at Howden Clough was photographed in June 1960.
Dr R. C. L./Author's collection

Two other changes in GNR signalling practices were also made following the Abbotts Ripton accident. A start had probably already been made towards the first change and that was distinguishing distant from stop (home and starting) signals. To conform to Board of Trade Requirements, distant signals had a V-shaped wedge cut from the left-hand end of the arms as seen by approaching drivers. The second alteration was a definite response to the accident, and that was the adoption of a green light

Above:
As well as single reinforced concrete signal posts, first erected during World War 1, the GNR also erected simple reinforced concrete brackets like this one photographed at Burgh-le-Marsh in August 1970, and more elaborate ones with a number of dolls.
M. A. King

for the all-clear indication in place of a white light. The GNR was the first company to make this change, and it was not until the publication of the Board of Trade's Requirements of 1893 that all British railways were made to follow suit. This also meant that from the 1850s until the Grouping, all GNR somersault signals had twin glass spectacles with one red and one blue/green glass.

Progressive though the GNR changes were immediately after the Abbotts Ripton accident, the disadvantage with the somersault signal design was that the spectacle casting and the arm could not be combined. When all other railways used separate spectacles and arms, this feature was of no consequence, but when George Edwards of the Gloucester Wagon Co led the way at the very end of the 1870s with the first combined arm and spectacle design and proved the advantages of this arrangement, the GNR's signal began to look awkward. Eventually every railway company apart from the GNR used semaphores which had the arm attached to the spectacle acting as a useful counter-weight. The nearest the GNR came to mimicking other railways' and signalling contractors' designs was in fixing the spectacle immediately adjacent to the arm, an arrangement which became standard for all new installations from the very end of the 19th century.

The final development of the somersault signal was the use of enamelled corrugated steel arms instead of wooden arms. The first examples were delivered and fitted to stop signals just three months after the Grouping, followed a few months later by yellow distant arms with a vertical black band on both the front and back.

The GNR was aware of the latest power signalling ideas in the first decade of the 20th century, but it was not tempted to implement any large scale schemes. Only a token gesture was made in 1920/1, when the new Signal Engineer, A. E. Tattersall, managed to have six American-style three-position upper quadrant arms installed at either end of Gas Works Tunnel, King's Cross. The experiment was probably not as comprehensive as he would have liked, being compromised by the fact that four of the new arms were used to give only two indications each.

2. Signalling Equipment, Electrical

The electric telegraph was used on most GNR lines as soon as they opened. On the main line, absolute block working was adopted comparatively early, at a time when the LNWR was using only a permissive system. In 1856 it was in use between London and Hitchin, twin-dial, single-needle instruments being used to communicate between signal stations. Unlike the LNWR system, however, the needles could not be pegged to a permanent indication, which was a cause of concern for the Railway Inspectorate.

In 1860 the system was causing delays and had to be modified so that more than one train travelling in the same direction could be allowed between signal stations. This was a retrogressive step but only a temporary one because after a particularly bad accident occurred in Welwyn Tunnel in June 1866 the GNR altered its signalling regulations and introduced new instruments that could give two permanent positive indications — Line Clear and Train on Line.

These 'new' instruments were fast becoming the standard single-needle peg-and-chain variety referred to in relation to many other companies throughout this book. When the decision was made at the very beginning of the 1870s to extend absolute block working to all passenger lines, these instruments were installed in all GNR signalboxes along with single-stroke bells, the domes attached beneath the electro-magnets in their mahogany cases.

After the Abbotts Ripton accident, the normal state of the line with no trains passing between signalboxes which until then had been Line Clear, was altered to become Line Blocked. Spagnoletti's patent needle units then became standard in all GNR pegging and non-pegging instruments, the three indications lettered on the dial. The only difference to similar units used by other railways was the nomenclature of the Train on Line indication. On GNR dials fitted to absolute block instruments this was lettered as Train Entered Section, and in permissive block instruments the terminology used was Line Occupied.

To ease the task of pegging and unpegging the drop handle of these instruments, the company's Telegraph Engineer, James Radcliffe, patented a trigger mechanism in 1885 (No 14,954) which could be manipulated by the signalman with one hand. All new instruments made for the company by various independent instrument makers were fitted with the new trigger, and older peg-and-chain units were also replaced, probably in the GNR's Telegraph Workshops at Retford.

As with all other railway companies using three-position instruments, the GNR used dial signals to reinforce the bell codes exchanged between signalboxes. Dial signals were sent on both pegging and non-pegging instruments by flicking the needle to either left or right depending on the message to be transmitted, before the needle was pegged to Line Clear or Train on Line. When the Railway Clearing House's new signalling regulations appeared in 1895 and were adopted by all companies, dial signals were abolished. Unlike the MR, the GNR found no further use for the drop handles on its non-pegging instruments and so introduced a shorter mahogany case approximately half the height of previous instruments, just large enough to accommodate the single-needle unit. The top sections of quite a number of old non-peggers and telegraph instruments were also adapted for this purpose, but equally many original full-sized instruments remained in use well into BR days.

The very last development of the GNR block instrument occurred just before the Grouping. To try to reduce the amount of space taken up by the instrumentation on a block shelf still further, a standard instrument case was fitted with a knob in place of Radcliffe's patent trigger and drop handle, a mechanical indicator as the pegging indicator in place of the single-needle unit, a single-needle unit positioned above this indicator to take the place of a separate non-pegging instrument, a block bell tapper to the right of the knob and a bell with its electro-magnets in a separate case suspended over the top of the case. The result was more a mutant instrument than a new design, the whole assembly comparing very poorly with Fletcher's LNWR 'combined' instrument of the 1890s, for example.

3. Signalling Equipment, Mechanical

The GNR installed its first interlocking lever frame in 1866 at Peterborough. This was supplied by Stevens & Sons. Before that date, individual levers and stirrup frame were used to operate points and signals. From 1866 until 1874, interlocking was confined mainly to junctions, but in 1874, having spent the previous five years conscientiously extending the block system, the company's Engineer, Richard Johnson, turned his attention to building substantial signalboxes equipped with fully interlocked lever frames at all important stations. By then Stevens & Sons was no longer the favoured contractor, and the GNR had already begun to award its contracts almost invariably to the lowest bidder. This policy meant that the company, at one time or another, employed all the most important firms who supplied mechanical signalling equipment. Easterbrook & Co, Ransomes & Rapier, Saxby & Farmer and McKenzie & Holland all did work for the GNR between 1870 and 1874. From then on until World War 1 the two latter firms were regularly engaged, but so too were the Gloucester Wagon Co, Dutton & Co, Evans O'Donnell, the Sykes Interlocking Co, F. A. Atkinson & Co and The Railway Signal Co. The lion's share of work between 1898 and 1903 was entrusted to The Railway Signal Co, but faithful McKenzie & Holland was still able to secure the contract in 1913 to signal the 'New Line' in Lincolnshire with its seven new signalboxes for a respectable £7,220 7s 2d.

Continued on page 81.

Traditional Signalling in Colour

Above:
An NER-pattern lower quadrant semaphore signal with the arm pivoted in a slot in the timber post. Provided by the signalling contractor McKenzie & Holland of Worcester, this example is preserved at Goathland on the North Yorkshire Moors Railway. *Author*

Above:
An example of the standard Stevens & Sons pattern lower quadrant semaphore still in use at Morar on the former NBR in 1966. *Trevor Sutcliffe*

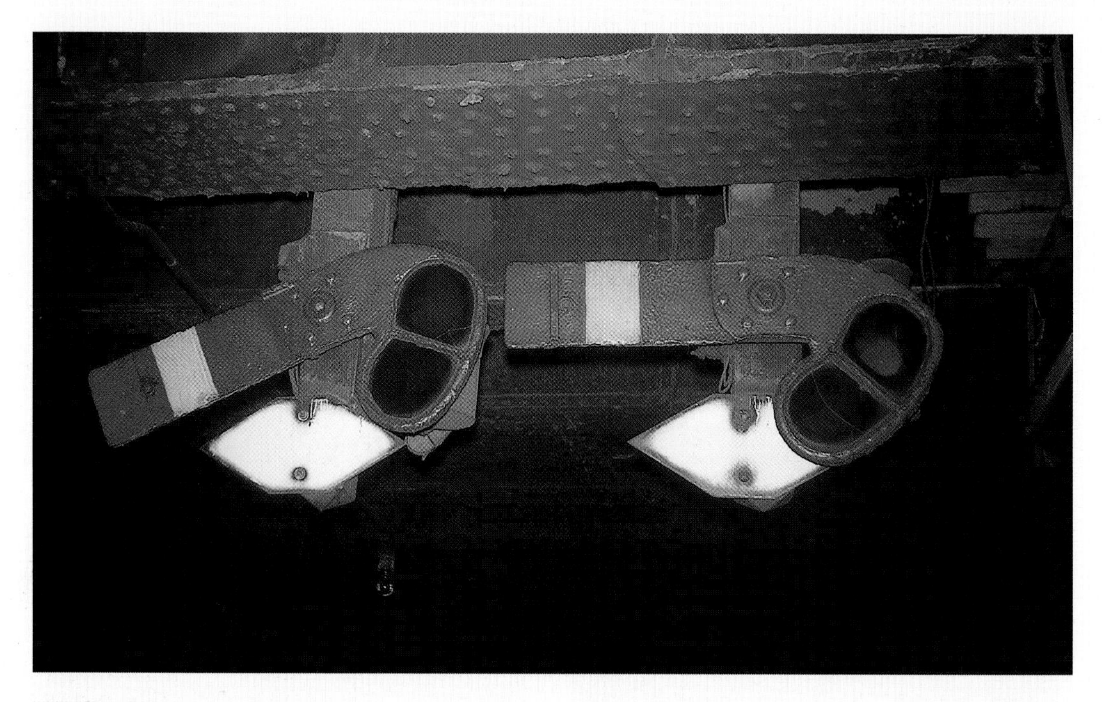

Above:
The L&Y's first standard pattern of lower quadrant semaphore with twin glass spectacle was developed directly from George Edward's single glass version marketed by the Gloucester Wagon Co and from 1881 by The Railway Signal Co. These L&Y examples under Trinity Street bridge, Bolton, were photographed in August 1967. *Trevor Sutcliffe*

Left:
FR lower quadrant semaphore at Bootle. This particular example had been provided with a mechanism for lifting the lamp into position from ground level, and the pulley wheel can just be made out slotted into the very top of the post.
Trevor Sutcliffe

Above left:
A GWR centrally pivoted lower quadrant semaphore at Droitwich Spa. This pattern of arm was used in places were the clearance below and either side of the signal was restricted. On some early examples, the arm was painted red and the central cast-iron boss picked out in white. *Author*

Above:
CLC lower quadrant home and distant signals at Cuddington in 1973. *Trevor Sutcliffe*

Left :
The twin glass spectacles of G&SWR lower quadrant semaphores were of an unique pattern with a circular red glass and an oval blue/green glass. This example was photographed at Glenwhilly in 1971.
Trevor Sutcliffe

Above left:
LSWR lower quadrant home and distant semaphores (with lower co-acting arm) protecting the up main line through Totton. *John Fairman/ Kidderminster Railway Museum*

Above:
Standard mid-1930s pattern upper quadrant semaphore mounted on a tubular steel post at Stallingborough on the former MS&LR. In the background is a well preserved example of that company's Type 2 signalbox (opened in 1884). *Author*

Left:
The British Pneumatic Railway Signal Co low-pressure pneumatic lower quadrant semaphores at Basingstoke (ex-LSWR) shortly before they were replaced by colour-light signals in 1966. The air cylinders are clearly visible a few feet beneath the spectacles. *John Fairman/ Kidderminster Railway Museum*

Left:
A photograph of the indicating unit of Edward Tyer's set of instruments (block bell above and separate plunger beneath), the design of which was perfected at the end of the 1860s and then used widely by many British railway companies. This example was last used on the former LBSCR at Crowborough. The lower of the two plungers lowered the white miniature semaphore (Line Clear) whilst the upper one raised it (Train on Line or Line Blocked). The miniature red semaphore was controlled by the signalbox in advance, in this case Eridge. *Author*

Below:
The block shelf in the preserved GWR/McKenzie & Holland signalbox on the Severn Valley Railway. To the left of signalman Pete Jordan's right hand is an example of Spagnoletti's 1863 patent block instrument (No 2297) with its 'keyless' or non-pegging partner to the right. The taller instrument visible was the design which emerged when the two separate pegging and non-pegging components were combined. *Author*

Above:
In some Sykes 'Lock & Block' installations, this type of instrument was used alongside the instrument physically connected to the operation of the signal lever. This particular design was essentially an updated version of Charles Walker's miniature semaphore instrument. The right-hand arm, worked mechanically by the bakelite knob to the right of the central bell tapper, transmitted either 'line clear' (arm lowered) or 'train on line' (arm raised) to the adjacent signalbox. The left-hand arm received those same indications from that neighbouring signalbox. *Author*

Above left:
A Spagnoletti patent single needle unit used by the GER in one of its speaking telegraph instruments. *Author*

Left:
Another Spagnoletti patent needle unit in a standard GNR pegging instrument fitted with Radcliffe's patent trigger mechanism. The GNR used the terminology 'train entered section' instead of the more usual 'train on line'. *Author*

Right:
This is an example of the last design of double-line block instrument supplied by Tyer & Co to the CR. Originally this instrument would have been fitted with two miniature semaphores but these were replaced by needles at some later date. Unlike the instruments purchased by the LBSCR, the plungers were colour-coded — white for 'line clear', red for 'train on line'. *Author*

Below:
The end of the quadrant plates of the 18-lever Stevens & Sons tappet frame (Patent 1870 No 746) installed in Sleaford North signalbox and brought into use in March 1882. Notice that the travel of the two distant signal levers (Nos 1 and 3) is greater than for the home signals (Nos 2 and 4). *Author*

Above:
Part of the 32-lever Saxby & Farmer Rocker & Gridiron type of frame in the GNR's 1877 signalbox at Stow Park. On the block shelf are standard GNR single-needle pegging and non-pegging block instruments and block bells. *Author*

Above:
The 12-lever LNWR (Webb) Tumbler frame in the preserved Pitsford Sidings signalbox on the Northampton & Lamport Railway. Behind the levers are the cast-iron description plates screwed to the wooden 'pulling board'. On the shelf are two examples of Fletcher's standard block instruments with later BR track circuit and signal repeaters. *Author*

Above:
Part of The Railway Signal Co/ Horwich lever frame in Blackburn East signalbox, photographed in December 1966. The illuminated track diagram in the background was a BR(LM) example, whilst just visible on the block shelf is a standard L&Y double line absolute block instrument. *Trevor Sutcliffe*

Right:
In the operating room of signalboxes the appearance of Dutton & Co lever frames was very distinctive, as is illustrated here in this example preserved at Llangollen station. In the background is a Tyer's No 9 Electric Train (key) Token instrument. *Author*

Above:
By the time the 1903 Westinghouse electro-pneumatic frame inside the ex-L&Y Bolton West signalbox was photographed in the spring of 1971, many of the miniature levers were out of use or had been removed. Nevertheless, the installation was still impressive. All the block instruments on the shelf, both absolute and permissive, were of BR standard pattern, designed by S. Williams, Signal Engineer of the London Midland Region in the 1950s.
Trevor Sutcliffe

Left:
West Silkstone Junction signalbox was an example of the MS&LR's design built at the end of the 1870s, marking the transition between Type 1 and Type 2 structures. Although by the time this photograph was taken in September 1981 the box had been extended at the non-staircase end, the hipped roof still retained one of its original large finials.
Trevor Sutcliffe

Above:
The Saxby & Farmer Type 9 signalbox provided at the L&Y's Thornton station in the late 1870s, photographed nearly one hundred years later, in 1973. *Trevor Sutcliffe*

Below:
The substantial rear wall of the FR's signalbox at Bootle, one of that company's Type 1 designs of the early 1870s. *Author*

Above:
Manea signalbox was built by McKenzie & Holland for the GER in 1883 and has subsequently been classified as a GE Type 3 structure. The arrangement of glazing bars in the operating room windows was original, but the Dexion steps were a strange late 20th century addition. *Author*

Left:
Lowfield signalbox, just south of Newark, was built by the GNR in 1887 to a pattern now described as Type 1b/Stow Park (revival). The decorative barge boards were just one of a number of patterns used by the company. *Author*

Right:
Photographed in the summer of 1968, Chester East signalbox was an example of the CLC Type 1a structures erected from the mid-1870s to 1903.
Trevor Sutcliffe

Below:
The signalbox at Windsor & Eton Riverside was an LSWR Type 2 design used by the railway company for structures erected between 1877 and 1884. The majority of Type 2 signalboxes had brick bases, but this was an example of an all-timber structure with vertical boarding. *Trevor Sutcliffe*

Left:
This signalbox at Hereford built in 1884 was originally named Ayleston Hill and is an example of a type derived directly from contemporary Saxby & Farmer designs. Only a handful of these LNWR/GWR Joint Type 2 signalboxes were built. *Author*

Right:
Park South signalbox, built in 1883 between Askam and Dalton, was one of the FR's handsome Type 3 designs. *Author*

Above:
Stockport No 2 was a large LNWR Type 4 structure opened in 1890. *Author*

Below:
Kew East signalbox was an NL Type 3b structure built at the start of the 20th century. *Trevor Sutcliffe*

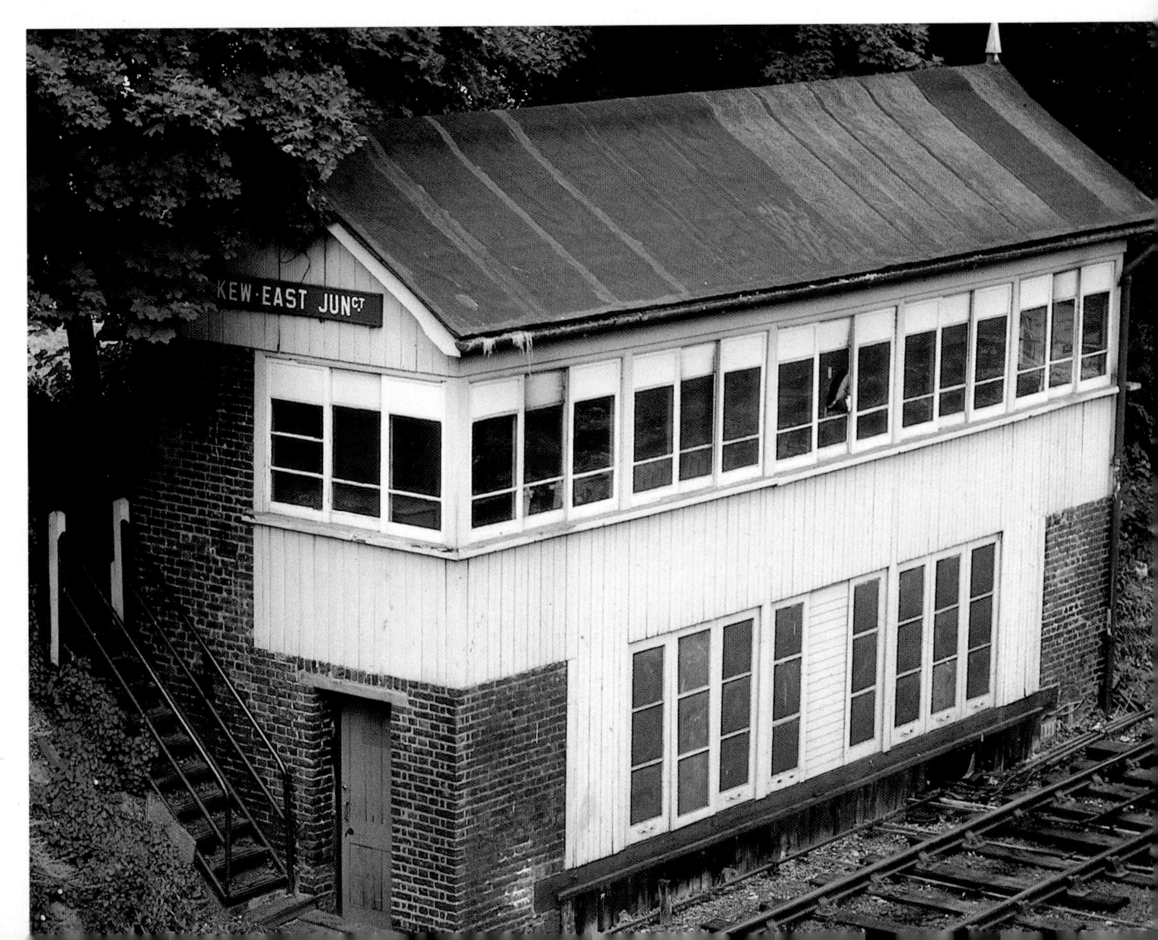

Above:
Sileby signalbox, between Leicester and Loughborough on the MR's main line, was a Type 2b pattern structure opened in December 1898 and closed in April 1987. *Author*

Above:
Abbey Foregate signalbox, Shrewsbury, was built in 1914 during the period when the GWR was responsible for signalling on the GW&LNWR Joint lines. It is one of the many variants of the GWR's handsome Type 7 design of signalbox. *Author*

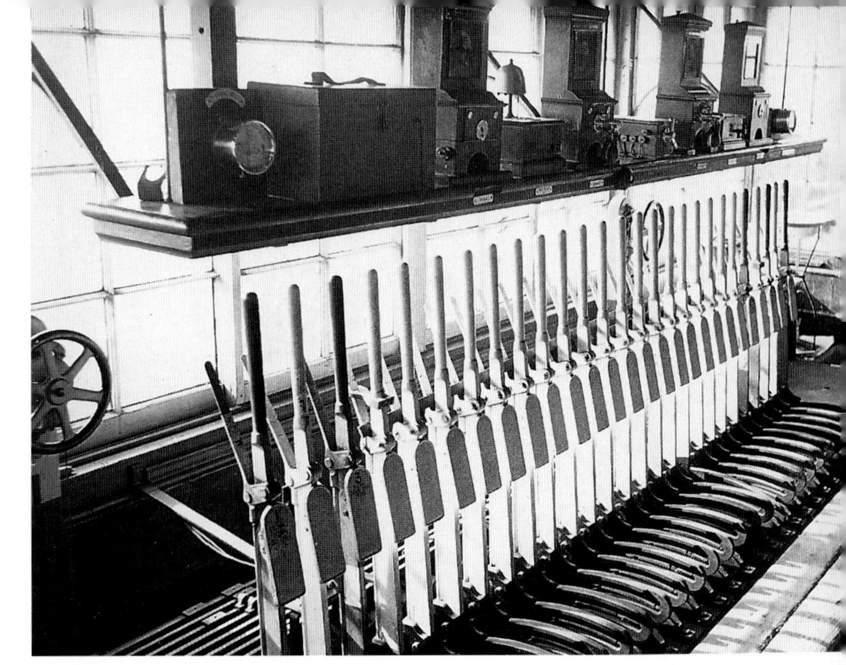

Right:
An example of a Saxby & Farmer 1874 Patent Rocker & Gridiron (No 294) installed in Breadsall signalbox in 1877. It has been calculated that approximately 2,500 frames of this pattern were made by the firm for use in this country and abroad. Amazingly it became the standard lever frame design in Belgium. Visible in front and to the right of each lever is the 'rocker' which rotated a 'gridiron' when the catch-handle was grasped, thus driving the locking immediately behind the levers. *W. H. A. Thompson/ D. J. Powell collection*

GNR signalboxes were showcases of the best of British non-conformity. At various times the company tried to standardise, but each time it lacked the the will to implement such a policy. Between 1870 and 1872, a number of frames with only a handful of levers were manufactured by the GNR itself, but as soon as frames with more levers were required, Johnson turned to contractors. In-house manufacture started again in the early years of the following decade, and the resultant tappet design remained in production until World War 1. From the end of the 1880s until about 1904 approximately 30 frames of a slightly different pattern were also made by the company, all of these confined to the Boston (Lincolnshire) District. From then on the GNR specified its own Saxby & Farmer 1905 Duplex frame derivative for all new jobs, and various signalling contractors manufactured and installed these for the company. But all the frames just mentioned only added to the wonderful variety of Victorian frame designs which, until the cull of main-line signalboxes in the 1970s, remained in daily use all over former GNR territory.

4. Signalbox Design

There was almost as much variety in GNR signalbox design as there was in the lever frames installed in them. The only difference was that, unlike lever frames, the GNR always specified signalboxes of its own pattern.

As with a number of main-line companies, the GNR built stages, towers and signal huts during the 1850s and into the early 1860s. Very few images survive of these structures, and the evidence suggests terminology was not consistently applied to be able to describe them accurately. Stages were usually erected at junctions and were probably little different from those of other companies, supporting semaphores, the levers to work them and the adjacent points, and a hut to house the telegraph instruments. Towers were probably similar to stages but, as their name suggests, much taller structures. Huts were just that, with room for just the instruments, signal lamps when not in use, and the signalman. Any levers were placed outside.

There is enough documentary evidence to suggest that from the mid-1860s a few Saxby-type glazed signalboxes began to appear, and by the end of the decade a standard all-timber structure with its gable parallel to the track was being constructed at a number of locations on the Main Line and Lincolnshire districts. Then, in 1871, a brand-new design made its appearance, setting the standard for all subsequent GNR signalboxes for at least two decades. The design varied both between districts and within them, but all had two features which led the Signalling Study Group to classify them as Type 1 signalboxes. All had gabled roofs at right angles to the track with a variety of different decorative barge boards, at least eight styles having been noted. Quite why this new design appeared fully formed from nowhere remains a mystery. When researching his history of GNR signalling, this author was unable to find any contemporary references to a definite decision to introduce it. As the GNR had only just made a commitment to

Above left:
St James Deeping signalbox was opened in July 1876, and displays just one of the variety of decorative barge boards used by the GNR. This particular 1976 photograph is interesting because it shows how the signalbox was built into the existing crossing keeper's house. *P. H. Wells*

Above:
Enfield Chase signalbox opened in 1910 to the GNR's last signalbox design, the Type 4a. It closed in September 1972. *M. A. King*

extending the block system and introducing interlocking throughout its system which would require a large number of new signalboxes, block instruments and locking apparatus, it is surprising the company should have opted for a comparatively lavish design. The majority of Type 1 signalboxes had brick bases, and the decorative barge boards and finials would only have added to the expense. A company such as the LNWR would certainly have seen the barge boards as an unnecessary luxury.

Nevertheless, hundreds were built and until 1883, when a simpler design made a brief appearance, there were no less than 18 distinct sub-types. The classification of the majority of these has been based on the arrangement of windows in the operating room and the distribution of panes within the sash units. These units varied in size from two panes wide by two panes high, to four panes high by three panes wide, with two categories having additional units beneath the main windows and another confined to the Yorkshire District having top-lights. For a detailed explanation and description the reader is referred to the author's *An Illustrated History of Great Northern Railway Signalling*, OPC, 2000.

In 1883 a simplified all-timber design started to appear, and this was used mainly on parts of the main line out of London that was in the process of being widened. It was also the start of the GNR's policy of providing separate signalboxes for up and down lines on its busiest sections. The Type 2 was almost identical to the GER's Type 2 signalbox, which both the GER and the GNR had agreed to use on the new sections of the GN&GE Joint Railway even though responsibility for the signalling was divided between the two companies on a geographical basis.

In 1892 this design was superseded by another all-timber signalbox, the Type 3. Once again, this type was most numerous on the main line between London and Peterborough, erected when additional slow and goods lines were laid. In place of horizontal boarding, the new design had vertical battened boarding, and although the width of the operating room window sashes varied (and with it the number of panes), all were four panes high.

During this time, the company had continued to build signalboxes of various Type 1 designs, and after 1887 a further three distinct varieties were added to the list. Finally, in 1907 the last new design appeared (Type 4), which did indeed become a standard, making its appearance on most parts of the GNR in both all-timber and brick-based form. The change of policy was undoubtedly due to the appointment of the company's first Signal Superintendent in 1902. Until then, signalling had been the sole preserve of the Engineer, delegating responsibility to District Engineers. However, as a gesture to the past, some of these new signalboxes were fitted with a decorative barge board based on one of the first designs of the 1870s.

MANCHESTER, SHEFFIELD & LINCOLNSHIRE RAILWAY/ GREAT CENTRAL RAILWAY

1. Signals

The Sheffield, Ashton-under-Lyne & Manchester Railway (SA&MR) was the first part of the Manchester, Sheffield & Lincolnshire Railway (MS&LR) to open in November 1841 between Manchester and Godley. It was originally just single track, which meant that the adoption of red, green and white flags for daytime use and the equivalent coloured lamps at night was vital for safe running. Fixed signals followed very rapidly, with a management decision to drive 'stakes' into the ground at the wayside stations on which lamps could be attached. When the line was extended to Dinting (then named Glossop) the following year, more permanent iron posts were erected to support revolving discs. These were painted red on one side to indicate stop, and green on the other to indicate proceed with caution. In line with the practice of the majority of Britain's other railways, if a driver could not see either side of the disc, then he assumed the line was clear.

The first three-position lower quadrant semaphore signals to be used on the MS&L (formed in 1846) were erected at Dukinfield Colliery in the summer of 1848, with distant (auxiliary) signals introduced shortly afterwards. From then on, semaphores were adopted for all new work, the section of line between Woodhouse Junction and Gainsborough which opened in July 1849 being equipped with them from the start. On these 'Cutts' signals, the action of moving the arm to one of its three possible positions also altered the aspect displayed by the lamp.

With the spread of block working and interlocking on the MS&L in the 1870s, the number of semaphore signals in use increased. Double-arm station semaphores were superseded by separate two-aspect home and starting signals for up and down lines, whilst two-position 'fish-tail' distant signals became standard equipment. As other companies began to adopt semaphores with the spectacle attached to the end of the arm, so did the MS&L, probably from the early 1890s. The spectacle held a single red glass which was moved clear of the lamp when the arm was pulled to the 'off' position to display its natural whitish light. The twin glass spectacle did not appear on the MS&L until the company was forced to abandon the white all-clear light following the Railway Clearing House recommendations of 1893. After this, arms were fitted with a spectacle reminiscent of that used by the GNR. This new standard signal design served the company through its change of name to the Great Central Railway (GCR) in August 1897 until the Grouping of 1923.

Above:
A signal bracket at Stalybridge photographed in the 1950s. The main post was reinforced concrete, the dolls were timber and the arms were the final standard design used by the GCR. *GCRS collection*

There were only three exceptions. The semaphores used in the GCR's power signalling scheme (see page 85) were of the British Pneumatic Railway Signal Co's (BPRS) own design, also supplied to the LSWR for use on its lines resignalled by the same firm. The automatic electro-gas signals installed on the stretch of main line between Whetstone and Ashby Magna in the first years of the 20th century were supplied by the Hall Automatic Signal Co to that firm's pattern, and finally the three-position upper quadrant semaphores brought into use at Keadby Bridge, Lincolnshire, in 1916 were of an American design supplied by the BPRS.

The GCR's Signal Engineer, A. F. Bound, was responsible for all these schemes which involved non-standard semaphores, and by the Grouping he was also one of a group of progressive signal engineers who advocated colour-light signals. He was unable to fulfil his ambitions before the GCR was absorbed into the LNER, but his appointment as that new company's Signal Engineer did ensure that the ex-GCR line between Marylebone and Neasden Junction and over the Wembley Exhibition loop was equipped with colour-light signals in 1923, the first on any British main line railway.

2. Signalling Equipment, Electrical

By 1845, Cooke & Wheatstone's electric telegraph had proved itself, and it was, therefore, not surprising that the SA&MR installed a circuit through its new single-track Woodhead Tunnel opened that year. From 1851, the Electric Telegraph Co was granted the right to install its equipment over most of the MS&L but, of course, the telegraph was not at first used to control the movement of trains between stations.

At the very end of 1857 the telegraph's functions were extended in this direction, but full block working was resisted for many years. After accidents in the mid-1860s, the Board of Trade Railway Inspectorate recommended its adoption, but to no avail. It was not until the very end of that decade that the line between Darnall and Orgreave Colliery, which included a tunnel, became the MS&L's first section to be controlled by the absolute block system. From then onwards, due in no small part to the steady pressure exerted by the Board of Trade on all the country's railways, and the reorganisation of the Electric Telegraph Co's business, the block system spread throughout the MS&L network. In 1870 the company's first Telegraph & Signal Superintendent was appointed, and gradually the MS&L acquired the instruments that were to serve it and its successors for the next one hundred years.

The type of instruments adopted were the standard single-needle variety as used by the neighbouring GNR and NER, amongst others, and single-stroke block bells of a distinctive split-case design, with the tapper offset to the right-hand side and bells of various shapes mounted at the top of a brass pillar which protruded through the top of the case. Line Clear and Train on Line were painted on the needle unit in the top right-hand and left-hand quadrants respectively, and when the third indication — Line Blocked — was adopted from the mid-1870s, this was painted just below the bottom of the needle when at rest. As was common with the majority of needle units supplied by Spagnoletti & Crookes, a printed ownership 'ribbon' appeared just above the Line Blocked lettering, the MS&L choosing to have its initials appear there in contrast to some other companies which opted for their full title (see p70).

Sometime probably in the late 1880s or early 1890s, the standard peg-and-chain arrangement was replaced, the drop handle being held in one of its two positions by a neat catch above the handle which was operated by the thumb of the signalman. This design continued into GCR days. When dial signalling on both the pegging and non-pegging instruments was abandoned following the introduction of the 1895 Railway Clearing House standard regulations, many non-pegging instruments were modified by emptying the case of all but the single-needle unit and replacing the lower front section with a new plain piece of mahogany. In contrast, the GNR physically cut off the lower section of its non-peggers, and it is useful for collectors of railwayana to note that the GCR did not use these type of short case 'repeaters'; these only appeared in ex-MS&L and GCR signalboxes after the Grouping.

The MS&L also operated goods lines on the permissive block system. At first the company's Telegraph & Signal Superintendent, R. S. Hampson, used a double-needle instrument of his own design patented in 1894 (No 690). Compared with the equivalent instruments manufactured by Tyer & Co, Hampson's was a crude piece of engineering. Its most clumsy feature was a slide which the signalman pulled out of the front section of the instrument. As more trains were signalled on to the already occupied goods line, the slide was pulled further out to indicate the number of trains travelling through the section. When the slide was fully extended it protruded from the case almost 10in, just

Above:
The interior of Marsh Junction signalbox, Grimsby, showing the type of mechanical lever frame the GCR adopted as its standard from about 1905. The most noticeable feature of the design were the 'jug handles' placed in front of the lever tops instead of the more usual catch-handles behind. The Railway Signal Co, McKenzie & Holland and Saxby & Farmer all manufactured frames of this design for the GCR, and it later developed into the LNER Standard with both conventional catch- and jug handles. On the shelf are standard MS&L/GCR block bells and instruments, with a Tyer's double-line permissive block instrument with the sloping front. *Author*

far enough to be inconvenient for the signalman. Probably after Hampson's promotion to Electrical Engineer in 1897 and the appointment of a new Signal Superintendent, Tyer & Co's single- and double-needle and co-operative permissive block instruments began to appear in GCR signalboxes.

Finally in this section, reference must be made to the all-electric signalling system installed at Immingham Docks in 1912. All semaphore signals and points were operated by electric motors, their actions controlled from six new signalboxes equipped with frames of pull-out slides supplied by the British Pneumatic Railway Signal Co, the largest (with 89 slides) being located in Immingham Reception 'box. These frames were almost identical to those used in that firm's low-pressure signalling installations (see page 86).

3. Signalling Equipment, Mechanical

The first point levers and mechanisms for changing the aspects of signals would have been simple blacksmith-made items. To reduce this bespoke work, the MS&L, as with many other railway companies in the late 1840s and 1850s, turned to the only major manufacturer of such equipment, Stevens & Sons of London. At first it supplied the MS&L with stirrup frames to operate its signals, and then a few lever frames when those became available.

However, progress with interlocking on the MS&L was slow, and it was not until the Regulation of Railways Act of 1873 required every railway company to submit annual updates of the progress

Above:
The non-standard Nottingham Victoria North signalbox completed in time for the opening of the GCR's London Extension in 1900. *Author's collection*

with installing interlocking and block working that the MS&L was forced to improve its record. Unlike its ally the GNR, the MS&L followed the example of the LNWR and decided to manufacture the necessary equipment in-house. In February 1875 a new signal and telegraph works was opened at Godley, and in 1877 Scatcherd, the company's Telegraph & Signal Superintendent, took out a provisional patent for a lever frame. The percentage of connections with passenger lines interlocked then rose from only 29% in 1875 to 50% in 1878.

This rate of progress inevitably slowed and by 1885 only 79% had been achieved. When the company submitted its statistics for the following year, however, the figure had shot up to 94%, reflecting a change of policy. Scatcherd's frame went out of production and The Railway Signal Co was employed to install its own design of lever frame in its own distinctive signalbox structures. By 1891 the MS&L had interlocked all passenger connections in accordance with Board of Trade Requirements. Three years later The Railway Signal Co was also entrusted with signalling the MS&L's London Extension, the largest such contract ever (£37,360), and the firm continued to be the company's sole mechanical signalling contractor until 1905.

By then a number of railway companies had been experimenting with power signalling, and when the plans for widening the lines east of Manchester (London Road) between Ardwick and Newton were drawn up in 1903, it was decided to signal the route with low-pressure pneumatically operated equipment following the LSWR's successful experience with BPRS. The GCR not only employed that firm but also poached its 'outdoor assistant', A. F. Bound, appointing him Assistant Signal Superintendent at the end of 1903, with promotion to head of the department in May 1906.

By then, work was well in hand with the resignalling, and in May 1905 the first signalbox with its BPRS frame of pull-out slides was brought into use. By 1906, 14 new signalboxes had been equipped with frames of pull-out slides. When operated, the slides allowed low-pressure air to pass to a valve next to the piece of lineside equipment. If all the interlocking was correct, the valve admitted air into the cylinder connected to the points or signals. Track circuits ensured slides could not be pushed back into the frame or pulled out again until a train had passed clear of the point or signal, returning the latter to danger automatically. The equipment and arrangements were the same as used by the LSWR on its lines between Woking Junction and Basingstoke (1903-6), except the GCR did not have the opportunity to install automatic signals between its relatively closely-spaced signalboxes. Finally, in 1909 an elevated signalbox with the same apparatus was switched-in at Manchester (London

Road), within sight of the LNWR's elevated cabin containing its own 'Crewe all-electric' power signalling system.

4. Signalbox Design

The first reference to the term 'signalbox' occurred in the MS&L minutes of March 1857 in connection with the opening of the Barnsley Branch. However, it is obvious that the company was slow to provide signalboxes as John Saxby would have recognised them until the 1870s.

When they did start to appear, the majority were of the railway company's own design. The first all-timber structures built throughout the 1870s were characterised by having hipped roofs with very large bulbous finials, and operating room windows with very tall but narrow panes of glass. On the front elevation of the signalboxes these panes were arranged in two rows. Where structures had to be built high to improve the signalmen's view of the track layout, signalboxes were elevated on substantial timber stilts. On these structures the bottom of the vertical battened boarding was finished with a saw-cut decorative pattern similar to that provided on station canopies.

By the end of the decade some of these Type 1 design signalboxes were being provided with operating room windows with a horizontal glazing bar, all sash units being of the same size on front and side elevations (see p74). Then, in the 1880s, the hipped roof was abandoned in favour of a gabled roof with decorative barge boards, similar to one of the numerous patterns used by the GNR. The vertical battened boarding was perpetuated, except in the gable ends it was set at a picturesque 45° either side of a prominent four-pane window light. These signalboxes were classified Type 2 by the Signalling Study Group. As with their predecessors, if a particularly tall structure was required, the operating and locking rooms beneath it were elevated on stilts with the boarding finished with a decorative frieze.

Not all signalling projects in this period could be fulfilled by the MS&L's own labour and equipment, and where the contractor Stevens & Sons was employed (1882-6), that firm provided a modified version of its own signalbox design with gabled roof and plain barge boards.

The next development of the MS&L's in-house design occurred about 1888. The size of the operating room windows was increased by introducing an additional row of panes in the sash units, and all-timber structures were built from panels with horizontal weatherboarding, each supporting three window sash units. The barge board details were also simplified and the gable ends lost their 45° boarding. A number of these Type 3 signalboxes were built with brick bases.

When The Railway Signal Co worked for the railway company in the 1880s, that firm had supplied all-timber signalboxes of its own design, with distinctive 'lace' pattern decorative barge boards and lower lights beneath the main operating room windows. When the same firm won the contract to signal the London Extension, however, signalboxes of the railway company's own pattern were erected. The new MS&L Type 4 was a refinement of the previous design with the ratio of height against width in the panes of glass in the operating room windows increased slightly, and all-timber structures built with horizontal lapped boarding. The majority of structures, however, had brick bases with locking room windows given flat stone lintels and sills. At Nottingham Victoria and London Marylebone, a special design of box was erected with prominent overhanging low-pitch hipped roofs.

The final variant, classified Type 5, was used for all new and replacement work from the beginning of the 20th century up to the Grouping and beyond until the end of the 1920s. The proportions of the operating room glass panes reverted to what they had been in the Type 3 signalboxes, and, most noticeably, the design of the decorative barge board was simplified by the removal of the middle nipple and the two holes previously located either side of the finial.

GREAT NORTH OF SCOTLAND RAILWAY

1. Signals

Very little is known about the earliest fixed signals on the GNSR. This is perhaps not surprising as even at the end of the 1870s there were only seven locations where points and signals were fully interlocked. In the 10 years following the 1889 Regulation of Railways Act the company was forced to upgrade both its signalling equipment and practices, and it was during this period that two standard patterns of semaphore signals with the arm attached to a twin glass spectacle began to appear. One had Stevens & Sons' standard but distinctive spectacle, whilst the other had what superficially looked like the same spectacle that was attached to

CR semaphore arms. Closer examination, however, indicates that it was bolted on to the same circular casting which surrounded the pivot on other Stevens semaphore arms and that the green glass was slightly longer than on CR signals. As was typical of Stevens signals, most were mounted on metal lattice posts.

2. Signalling Equipment, Electrical

When W. H. Preece presented his paper 'On Railway Telegraphs and the Application of Electricity to the Signalling & Working of Trains' to the Institution of Civil Engineers at the beginning of 1863, mention was made that Edward Tyer's needle instruments had been in use for some years on the GNSR. Mr Gilbert, the company's Telegraph Inspector at the time, was not convinced about the reliability of the equipment, although he did concede the exchange of

Left:
A GNSR semaphore with small arm photographed at MacDuff on 13 June 1960. The style of cast-iron finial betrays the manufacturer — Stevens & Sons.
Author's collection

Below:
The GNSR Type 2 signalbox at Alford, an example of a pattern built between 1884 and the end of the century. Next to it the home signal sports a semaphore arm with an instantly recognisable and characteristic Stevens & Sons spectacle.
Ian Allan Library

Above:
The handsome GNSR Type 3 signalbox at Craigellachie, photographed in 1962.
Real Photographs/Ian Allan Library

Above:
A dramatic and useful view of the co-acting GNR-pattern somersault signals at Gayton Road on 28 September 1958. The reinforced concrete post was a standard M&GNJR casting, but unusually this one was painted white. Most were left in their natural state. *A. G. Ellis*

bell codes was useful when the needles were not working properly. His concern stemmed from faults caused by lightning which although did not usually lead to permanent damage, had recently completely destroyed a pair of instruments.

How extensive Tyer's system on the GNSR was by that date is not known, but the railway continued to patronise the firm and eventually improved the safety of its single-line sections by installing Tyer's Electric Train Tablet system. Because tablets had to be passed between train crew and signalmen by hand, trains not stopping at passing places on single lines had to slow so this exchange could be carried out safely. To speed up the whole operation, the Locomotive Superintendent, James Manson, developed a mechanical apparatus at the end of the 1880s which enabled the exchange of tablets when trains were travelling at up to 60mph. The first passing places were fitted with the apparatus in May 1889.

3. Signalling Equipment, Mechanical

As mentioned above, the GNSR was very slow in introducing interlocking equipment. In 1875 a mere 12% of all locations had been tackled, and the year before the 1889 Regulation of Railways Act little more than 50% had been achieved. The main signalling contractor employed by the company was Stevens & Sons, with a limited amount of work also going to The Railway Signal Co. Not surprisingly, most frames were of both Stevens' Glasgow Old and Glasgow New Patterns manufactured between 1870 and 1949.

4. Signalbox Design

At the Grouping of 1923, the GNSR reported that it had 127 signalboxes in use on its system. Some of those had substantial masonry bases of either brick or stone, others were all-timber structures, and many were made up of parts of earlier signalboxes. In essentials, they were simple buildings which changed stylistically very little over the years.

The first recognisable signalboxes appeared in the 1870s with hipped roofs and operating room windows made up of individual sash units two panes wide by three panes high. The same glazing was used until the end of the century when the vertical glazing bar in the top third of the sash was omitted, along with the horizontal glazing bar in the bottom third of the window. From the middle of the 1880s, almost all signalboxes were all-timber buildings with horizontal weatherboarding and simple gabled roofs, but hipped roofs made a return in 1896 for the final batch of new signalboxes.

MIDLAND & GREAT NORTHERN JOINT RAILWAY

1. Signals

The Midland & Great Northern Joint Railway (M&GNJR) did not exist until 1893, when the Midlands & Eastern Railway (M&ER) was brought together with the Eastern & Midlands Railway (E&MR) under the joint control of the GNR and MR. Responsibility for signalling the M&ER had been divided between the two companies since 1867, and by the beginning of the 1890s standard MR signals (and signalboxes) had appeared on the line between Peterborough and Kings Lynn, with equipment of GNR design being used on the line between Bourne and Sutton Bridge. As the parent companies' signal design was upgraded, so the signals were altered on the M&ER. The MR continued to supply its latest designs until 1901, explaining why photographs of M&GNJR stations with MR signals invariably show arms with twin glass spectacles.

On the E&MR's lines east of King's Lynn, the signals remained of the slot-in-the-post variety supplied by Saxby & Farmer until the M&GNJR was formed and the GNR took over responsibility for all Joint line signalling. From then on, standard GNR somersault signals were installed, the spectacles mounted a few feet lower than the arm. By the turn of the century the spectacles were being fixed adjacent to the arms, in line with current GNR practice.

From 1900 GNR signal fittings became standard throughout the M&GNJR, and there were examples of new GNR somersault arms being fitted to existing MR posts and bracket signals. In 1922 the GNR ordered its first enamelled steel arms, and eventually a number of these found their way onto the M&GNJR. Inevitably, former MR signals remained in use (those at Sutton Bridge surviving until closure of the network in 1959), but there was one interesting hybrid signal born of both parent companies. The MR used a distinctive hammerhead-shaped arm for 'calling-on' purposes, and this design was adopted by the M&GNJR but modified as a centrally pivoted somersault arm.

Another development particularly associated with the M&GNJR was, of course, the reinforced concrete signal post. William Marriott, the company's Locomotive Superintendent, took out a number of patents, and manufacture of signal posts, brackets, telegraph poles, fence posts, sleepers and

Above:
Another tall reinforced concrete post supporting an enamelled steel stop arm and the unique M&GNJR pattern somersault calling-on arm.
Real Photographs/Ian Allan Library

Above:
The fireman of ex-GER 4-4-0 No 62523 collects the single-line tablet from the signalman at Runton West Junction on 17 June 1952. The signalbox was of the M&GNJR's Type 1b. *L. R. Peters*

many other items took place during World War 1. Experiments were even made with hollow posts. The claims made for reinforced concrete was its strength and durability, but in an article in the 1918 *Railway Magazine* mention was also made of its 'pleasing' appearance, especially when coloured, although this was confined to station nameboards rather than signal posts and brackets.

The GNR somersault semaphore remained the M&GNJR's standard signal for running lines until the LNER assumed responsibility for operating the network in 1936.

2. Signalling Equipment, Electrical

With no substantial part of the M&GNJR opened before the mid-1860s, the predominantly single lines of the various constituent companies were operated by the electric telegraph and Staff working from the beginning. The E&MR adopted Tyer's tablet system when that became available at the end of the 1870s, and from 1893 it became the standard for controlling all M&GNJR single lines. Both Tyer's No 1 and No 6 instruments were used, and the railway company was particularly conscientious in ensuring the levers working the starting signals were interlocked with the instruments. By 1922 every signal controlling entry into a single-line section was linked with the actions of Tyer's instrument. After 1906, the exchange of tablets was improved with the installation of Whitaker's patent exchange equipment.

On double-track sections, absolute block working was in force using standard GNR single-needle instruments and block bells, many instruments clearly marked 'M&GNJR'.

3. Signalling Equipment, Mechanical

Almost nothing is known about the original equipment used between 1858, when the first short section of the future M&GNJR opened, and the start of a definite programme of interlocking to Board of Trade standards from the 1880s onwards. On the Peterborough and King's Lynn section under the care of the MR, that company's standard 'Tumbler' frames were brought into use in new signalboxes between 1889 and 1892. On the Bourne to Sutton Bridge (exclusive) section, which was the responsibility of the GNR, interlocking was carried out by The Railway Signal Co in the 1890s using its standard frame design. Signalling on the E&MR was also put into the hands of contractors, the majority of this work apparently going to Saxby & Farmer, who supplied and fitted examples of its 1874 Rocker & Gridiron and 1888 Duplex frames.

After the formation of the M&GNJR the signal shops at Melton Constable were enlarged, and as both MR and Saxby & Farmer frames appeared in new post-1893 signalboxes, it is likely that frame parts were recycled.

4. Signalbox Design

Prior to 1893, the most obvious visual indication of the division of signalling responsibility was the design of signalboxes. On the section maintained by the MR, signalboxes of that company's standard Type 2 pattern were provided. On lines under GNR signalling control, signalboxes were built to that company's standard which The Signalling Study Group classified GN Type 1/RSCo. The only feature that distinguished these structures from the GNR signalbox designs they were based on was the decorative barge boards of The Railway Signal Co's standard pattern. Apart from this, and using this author's classification which appeared in his *An Illustrated History of Great Northern Railway Signalling* (OPC, 2000), the panelled brick-based signalboxes were identical to the GN Type 1b/ Stow Park design, and the all-timber structures were the same as the Type 1b/ Gainsborough pattern. On the lines east of King's Lynn, which were built by several companies and formed part of the E&MR between 1883 and 1893, the signalboxes were of various designs. Elevated structures are known to have been provided at Sheringham and Holt, but few photographs of others survive, and therefore no classification has been possible.

Within a year of the formation of the M&GNJR, a standard all-timber signalbox design was in production at Melton Constable. This was used mostly on single lines that were being upgraded to double-track routes. The structural vertical posts were visible on the exterior with vertical boarding fitted between them, and most had operating room window sash units three panes wide by four panes high. All had gabled roofs decorated with what has been described as 'bit & tongue' pattern barge boards. About 1903 this standard signalbox design was modified when all but the corner posts of the timber frame were covered with horizontal lapped boarding. All other details remained the same.

LONDON & NORTH EASTERN RAILWAY

Barely two years after the Grouping during the summer of 1925 the former GER station at Cambridge was resignalled. The project was very much a result of one man's enthusiasm for power signalling. The new Signal Engineer for the LNER's Southern Area, A. F. Bound, when working for the GCR had been responsible for the impressive pneumatic scheme brought into use in 1906 between Ardwick and Newton, east of Manchester, and then the equivalent all-electric system installed at Immingham Docks in 1912. By comparison, the Cambridge job was a simple one. The control equipment, supplied by the British Power Railway Signal Co, was identical to that used in Lincolnshire but the two-position semaphores were the lower quadrant equivalents of the American pattern three-position upper quadrants installed by the SECR at Victoria station with the same enamelled tapering corrugated steel arms.

Left:
Sessay Wood (later renamed Pilmoor South) signalbox on the main line north of York photographed in December 1933 11 months after it opened. It was equipped with a 15-lever McKenzie & Holland mechanical frame as well as a signalling panel. It was mainly the roof and the use of brick that made this structure reminiscent of contemporary suburban or 'Garden City' domestic architecture. *LNER official photograph/ Ian Allan Library*

Right:
In the summer of 1925, five mechanical signalboxes were replaced by just two, Cambridge North and Cambridge South, both fitted with control equipment supplied by the British Power Railway Signal Co. Shown here are most of the 72 pull-out slides in the North box. (The South box had 128 slides.) The signalman in the background has his hand on the GER's standard Tyer & Co's 'flapblock'. This photograph was taken in May 1953. *R. E. Vincent*

Bound left to become the new Signal & Telegraph Engineer of the LMS in 1929, and the torch of innovation at the LNER was taken up by his assistant, A. E. Tattersall. At the Grouping, Tattersall had been Signal Superintendent on the GNR, and then in 1928 he was promoted to the Northern Area of the LNER. It was that Area's good fortune, because no other part of the LNER was so forward looking in matters of signalling. King's Cross was resignalled in 1932 with colour-light signals operated from a frame of 232 miniature levers, and four-aspect colour-light signalling was brought into use on the ex-GER between Gidea Park and Shenfield at the very beginning of 1934, but the real technological leap was made in Tattersall's Area. In 1933, in place of a separate track diagram and lever frame, or its equivalent, he installed a panel into the cabin of Goole Swing Bridge on

Above:
A 1938 photograph of the well-proportioned signalbox at Hull Paragon station, built to house the LNER's latest route setting panel, then the most advanced piece of railway signalling equipment in the world. The panel was brought into use on 23 April 1938. *LNER official photograph/ Ian Allan Library*

which was a representation of the layout with the signal switches positioned next to the icons of the signals they controlled. The point switches were arranged in a row along the bottom of the panel. His next step was to marry the panel/track diagram to the GWR's pioneering work with route-setting, and in November 1933 a new signalbox with the true predecessor of all subsequent signalling panels was brought into use at Thirsk on the ex-NER main line. This was a decisive break with tradition, and to confirm its position at the forefront of signalling developments, Tattersall brought another route-setting, relay-interlocking signalling panel into use at Hull Paragon station in April 1938. Because of the complexity of the layout and the number of routes which could be set (230 in all), the design of this panel was altered. The route switches were arranged on a sloping fascia beneath the vertical illuminated track diagram with the emergency switches in between. This arrangement became the model for all subsequent Westinghouse standard OCS (One Control Switch) panels. A year later, a similar panel was commissioned at Northallerton, and, if war had not intervened, York station would have been next in line for resignalling. That had to wait until 1951.

The style of signalboxes these panels were installed into was also modern. Thirsk and Hull had the look of airfield control towers, with the operating room perched on top of a long single-storey brick base. At Northallerton the brick base was taller and, despite the threat of war, the operating room was provided with the same large windows and a hipped roof covered with fired clay tiles. This design echoed other stylish mechanical signalboxes recently erected along the same stretch of main line in the comfortable — and very English — 'Garden City' school of architecture.

3
The Southern Railway

Of all the post-1923 railway companies, the Southern Railway (SR) probably had more diversity of signalbox, block instrument and lineside equipment design than any other. This did not reflect the pre-Grouping constituent companies' lack of direction, but more the fact that they had not only been in the forefront of innovations from a very early date but had also made significant investment in the latest technology in the 1850s and '60s, which meant that by 1923 the SR inherited some of the earliest signalling equipment anywhere in the country. On the lines of the former London, Brighton & South Coast Railway (LBSCR), there were still examples of the country's very first signalboxes developed by John Saxby in the mid-19th century. All over the SR there were also thousands of block instruments of the same period still in everyday use. Although most had been modified to conform to later standards, they were still fundamentally instruments of an age when signalmen were considered illiterate and needed miniature semaphore arms to tell them what their outdoor signals should be indicating to the driver of an approaching train. Of those signals, the SR was fortunate in inheriting very few semaphores of mid-19th century design, the majority of its lower quadrants combining both the spectacle plate for the coloured glasses and the arm, a development of the late 1880s and '90s.

Although most signalling equipment on the new SR dated from the period 1860-1900, the London & South Western Railway (LSWR), LBSCR and the South Eastern & Chatham Railway (SECR) had shown a willingness to install a number of 'power signalling' schemes in the first years of the 20th century, and that desire to modernise passed into the new company. By the time nationalisation swallowed up the SR in 1948, the company had some of the most modern signalling equipment in use of any British railway, a testament to the vision of its interwar management.

LONDON & SOUTH WESTERN RAILWAY

1. Signals

According to railway historians, the LSWR used fixed signals from the opening of its main line between London and Southampton in 1840. The signal consisted of a circular disc and separate lamp, a not unusual combination for the time, but the overall design developed by Albinus Martin was unique.

Quite what the very first form of the signal looked like is not known, but just before the LSWR adopted the semaphore as standard in the early 1860s, there were three distinct types of Martin's signal in use. The simplest of the three was what he described as a 'signal for one road only'. A circular metal rim frame was mounted on top of a post which could be rotated through 90° on a vertical axis. Attached to the frame was half a circular disc, originally canvas and later sheet metal, both sides painted red. As was normal on most railways at this date, the line was considered all-clear when the disc was turned edge-on so that it could not be seen by the footplate crew. The danger indication was with the half disc in the left-hand quadrant of the rim as seen by an approaching train. If a driver spotted a disc with the right-hand quadrant covered, he knew the signal did not apply to him. A lamp was positioned just below the disc capable of showing a red or white light. In the final form of this signal, the disc was fixed to the top of a metal framework which was itself attached to a small platform. The platform was aligned with the centreline of the post so that, when the lamp was placed on this platform, it too was centred with the post and the disc.

The second form of Martin's signal was used at junctions alongside the one just described. This special junction signal also had a red half disc on a rim frame, but immediately below it was a smaller disc painted green with a black centre. Danger was indicated with both discs facing the driver, and when the post was rotated through 90° both discs appeared edge-on to approaching trains, indicating all-clear. The only purpose of the smaller disc was to warn

Above:
This photograph will be familiar to many signalling enthusiasts, but it is useful in illustrating the pneumatically operated lower quadrant semaphores installed on the LSWR's main line between Woking Junction and Basingstoke. These examples at the latter were brought into use in 1906 and were photographed on 17 August 1962. *J. Scrace*

drivers of the junction ahead. At night, two lamps came into operation. The higher one displayed the standard red for danger or white for all-clear, whilst the lower one shone a green light, no matter what the top lamp was displaying.

At a normal double-track junction there would have been two pairs of posts erected either side of the main line close to the junction points. As seen by approaching trains, either on the main line or the branch, the twin disc junction signal was located to the left of a single disc signal. Both single disc signals controlled movements on the main line, whilst one twin disc signal controlled movements on to the branch, and the other movements from the branch on to the main line. Obviously, the signalman had to make sure that one of the pair of signals always displayed danger. It is unlikely there was ever any interlocking between Martin's junction signals or between the signals and the points to which they referred.

At double-track passenger stations, a third variation of Martin's signal was erected. As with double-arm station semaphores it controlled trains approaching in opposite directions, but unlike those semaphores Martin's signal was not used in quite the same way. It was not intended to signal trains into and out of the station, but to stop them entering when shunting was taking place on the through lines. As with the other signals described earlier, the station variant had the usual half disc attached to a circular rim frame which could be rotated through 90° on a vertical axis. If the lines were unobstructed and trains could enter the station unhindered, the signal was turned so that it could not be seen by approaching trains from either direction. Unlike Martin's other signals, however, the frame of the disc was mounted so that it could also rotate like a wheel. A rope was attached around the circumference of the frame and operated by a pulley arrangement from the base of the post. When the half disc was pulled into the top quadrant of the frame this indicated that both through lines were blocked. If the half disc was pulled into the left quadrant of the frame as seen by the approaching driver, this indicated his line was blocked but the other line was clear. And if that same driver saw the disc in the right-hand quadrant, he knew it was safe for him to enter the station, but the opposite line was blocked. At night a white light indicated all-clear and a red meant danger, one or two lamps being used to project these aspects depending on the design of lamp used.

Despite the sophistication of Martin's signals, the LSWR must have started to use standard semaphore signals from at least the early 1860s when the company's Superintendent of Telegraphs,

W. H. Preece, brought his miniature semaphore block instrument into use (see below). Once this happened, Martin's discs were relegated to serve as auxiliary or distant signals, and by the 1880s they had almost certainly all been displaced. As the LSWR used signalling contractors for the majority of its signalling work from the 1860s onwards, the earliest semaphores were probably of those firm's own designs. There are photographs of semaphores pivoted in square-section timber posts, but by the end of the century the majority of the company's semaphore signals were mounted on individual metal lattice posts or brackets and gantries with lattice dolls. The preference for such structures was almost certainly inherited from the company's favoured signalling contractor, Stevens & Sons.

When slot-in-the-post signals were gradually replaced by semaphores with arms attached to twin glass cast-iron spectacles incorporating the pivot for mounting on the front face of the signal post, the LSWR appear to have settled on a design which was supplied no matter which contractor had successfully secured a signalling contract. The spectacle was almost identical to that used by the SECR and may have been a standard Stevens & Sons pattern. Although the majority of LSWR semaphore arms were wooden, the company did install a number of corrugated steel examples, and photographs taken in the British Railways era show that enamelled arms with flat faces and edges bent at 90° were also fitted at some date (almost certainly not in LSWR days).

Finally, mention should be made of the attempt made at the very end of the 19th century by the LSWR along with the LBSCR, SECR and the GER, to distinguish the night-time indication of distant signals from those displayed by stop signals. With the publication of the 1893 Board of Trade Requirements, any company still using a white light as an all-clear indication was obliged to alter this to a green one. From then on, railways had to standardise on just two coloured lights for all their running line signals — red for danger and green for all-clear. White was to be used as a 'back-light' to indicate to signalmen who could not see the front face of any signal, that the red light was showing correctly. When the signal was pulled to all-clear, the light was obscured, so that if the signal had not been pulled but the light could not be seen, they knew the lamp had gone out. The major weakness of the 1893 decision was that the opportunity was not taken to give the distant signal a different aspect when in the 'on' position. Showing a red indication, a distant signal could be passed safely, the driver knowing that one or more stop signals ahead were against him. However, if a driver passed a stop signal at danger he and his train were in immediate danger.

Keen to help drivers distinguish between stop and distant signals at night the LSWR, along with the other three companies named above, adopted the Coligny-Welch lamp on a number of its distant signals. This device was simply an extension to a standard lamp case which protruded to the right of the main lamp as seen by approaching drivers into which an arrow-shaped slot was cut. By means of a reflector and mirror, light passed through the arrow, which remained illuminated whether the distant signal was 'on' or 'off'.

2. Signalling Equipment, Electrical

In 1860 the LSWR appointed William H. Preece as its Superintendent of Telegraphs, which immediately put the company in the vanguard of block signalling developments. Preece had come from the Electric Telegraph Co where he would have been familiar with his colleague Edwin Clarke's work in persuading the LNWR to install its 'Two Mile Telegraph' in the mid-1850s. The fundamentals of this system using twin-needle instruments was to inform signalmen whether the line was clear or blocked. Preece preferred a system that instructed signalmen what indication their station semaphore should display at any given time. To put his principle into practice he developed and patented in 1862 (No 77) three electrical devices. The most striking was a wooden case, containing an electro-magnet, from which protruded a tall metal post, at the top of which was a single miniature semaphore arm. The second device was also worked by an electro-magnet, operating an indicator with two possible indications — 'off' or 'on'. The third device was a miniature lever, described in the 1862 patent as a 'switch key'.

When a train entered the section between stations, the signalman who was to receive the train operated Preece's miniature lever which raised the miniature semaphore arm to 'danger' at the end from which the train was being sent. This prompted the signalman there to place his signal to 'danger', thus preventing another train from entering the section. Whilst the miniature semaphore arm was in the 'danger' position, the indicator on the second device at the far end of the section displayed the word 'on', to confirm to the signalman there who was awaiting the train that the miniature semaphore at the other end was displaying the correct indication and the line was blocked. Once the train had arrived safely,

Left:
Originally this LSWR Type 1 signalbox at Dean had the diagonal crossed bracing in the timber frame of the operating room exposed. The horizontal weatherboarding added at the end of the 19th century had the effect of making the structure closer in style to signalboxes of the 1860s. *J. Scrace*

the signalman put his miniature lever to the 'off' position, (which would be indicated by the word 'off' in the other instrument), and the miniature semaphore at the end from which the train had come would disappear into its metal post — the accepted 'all-clear' position — telling the signalman there that he could once again lower his outdoor semaphore because the line was clear.

Preece continued to develop his system and in 1865 patented a 'lock & block' version (No 2016). Once put to 'danger', the miniature lever was locked in position until the train passed over a treadle which freed it for another 'line clear' pull. The next change was to incorporate the single-stroke bell and its electro-magnets into the same case as the 'on/off' indicator. This gained a circular face behind which the single-stroke bell was mounted. In 1866 Preece produced a one-wire (momentary current) version of his semaphore instrument, and in 1872 the miniature semaphore, bell and 'on/off' indications were all incorporated into a single wooden case. The 'on/off' indicator and bell were mounted on top of the case behind a semi-circular glass-fronted screen. The miniature semaphore and post were also redesigned so that the 'all-clear' indication was displayed with the arm inclined at 45°. The brass post and arm were contained within a circular glass-fronted aperture. Before long, the same amalgamation of parts was applied to the original 1862 'three-wire' system. In this redesign, the miniature semaphore arm was placed in a rectangular glass-fronted aperture.

3. Signalling Equipment, Mechanical

As mentioned earlier, Stevens & Sons was the favoured contractor for signalling work on the LSWR and some of the first interlocking lever frames installed in the 1860s were of Stevens' hook design. In early 1867 a signalbox erected on a gantry across the tracks was brought into use at Waterloo, London, the cabin being fitted with 47 levers. When that firm introduced its more robust tappet design in 1870, frames of that pattern began to appear on the LSWR, and in the 1880s it was adopted by the railway company as a standard piece of equipment no matter which firm was awarded a signalling contract. The frame was used both for new work and as a replacement for Saxby & Farmer's 1867 patent frames where they had been installed.

In addition to all this well-tried and tested equipment, however, the LSWR was one of a number of railways at the very end of the Victorian era to feel confident enough to experiment with power signalling. This was not just for the sake of experimentation, however. The real incentive was the desire, as with many railway companies at that time, to find more efficient and economical ways of dealing with an increasing number of trains.

In October 1901 a signalbox containing a frame of pull-out slides supplied by the British Pneumatic Railway Signal Co was brought into use at Grateley,

Left:
The LSWR all-timber Type 4 signalbox at Bentley, photographed on 3 June 1970. *J. Scrace*

on the main line just northeast of Salisbury. When pushed or pulled horizontally, the slides allowed air into a closed circuit which in turn let air into cylinders ('motors') which operated the signals and points. The installation was to test the equipment with a view to using it at Salisbury where the company planned to rebuild the station. Having proved a success, two new signalboxes were erected at Salisbury, each equipped with pneumatic frames of 64 slides, and they were commissioned in November 1902. Further installations followed at Staines, and then the company turned to what was probably the most ambitious power signalling project until the SR resignalled the Brighton main line in the 1930s: on the 24 miles of mainly quadruple track between Woking Junction and Basingstoke, 12 signalboxes were equipped with pneumatic frames, and, on the long stretches of intermediate plain track, automatic signals were erected. By the end of 1906, this work was complete. The final pneumatic scheme brought into use, two years before World War 1 stopped any further resignalling projects, was at Clapham Junction, where five new signalboxes were commissioned.

4. Signalbox Design

By 1922 the LSWR calculated that it had 531 signalboxes in operation. George Pryer, in his latest book *Signal Boxes of the London & South Western Railway* (Oakwood Press, 2000), identified a number of substantial signalboxes of the 1860s which survived until recently. Of those, some were obviously derived from Saxby's designs, whilst others were built entirely of brick with hipped or gabled roofs and operating room windows set into the walls. In this form they were very similar to the first generation of NER signalboxes. The LSWR continued to build a number of other non-standard designs over the years, and signalling contractors added to the variety by erecting their own patterns.

The first distinctive design to be built in any numbers appeared in the first years of the 1870s. This design had a masonry base and a timber superstructure with small operating room windows tucked under the eaves of a shallow hipped roof. Originally the diagonal cross-bracing of the superstructure was exposed on the exterior giving the signalboxes a certain 'cottage orné' appearance, heightened by a decorative awning under the eaves. Eventually, horizontal weatherboarding was nailed over the bracing and the awnings were removed, giving them a more utilitarian aspect.

The next development at the end of the 1870s, and one which was common to many railways of the period, was a design with enlarged operating room windows. The individual sash units were increased in height so that the windows were three panes tall. The use of a decorative awning at eaves level was perpetuated on these Type 2 structures, most of which had external horizontal weatherboarding. In the subsequent Type 3 design of the 1880s and '90s, the number of panes in the operating room windows were increased again, so that they were four panes high. One variant of the design also had additional top-lights fitted under the eaves.

The final LSWR signalbox design (Type 4) which appeared in the mid-1890s was completely different from its predecessors save for the use of a shallow hipped roof. The majority were built of brick to roof level, with a solid piece of masonry in the centre of the front of the operating room. The windows then appeared to be wrapped around the corners. The sash units were two panes high by two panes wide, elliptical framing added to the tops of the upper most panes giving them a distinctly Saxby & Farmer Type 5 feel.

LONDON, BRIGHTON & SOUTH COAST RAILWAY

1. Signals

The first type of fixed signals used by the London & Croydon (L&CR) and the London & Brighton (L&BR) railways consisted of flat circular discs which could be turned through 90° to give two indications. On the L&CR single discs were used, but the L&BR (apparently from its opening in 1841) erected signals with two flat discs connected by a horizontal pole attached to a vertical post. Unlike the L&CR discs, which pivoted on a vertical axis, the L&BR discs could be rotated through 90° in the horizontal plane to give two indications: 'danger' with the discs vertical, facing the driver, and 'all clear' with the discs flat or parallel with the ground and almost invisible to the approaching train. At night a lamp was used to give the indications — a red light for stop, a white light for all-clear.

In the same year that the L&BR opened, Charles Gregory, Engineer of the L&CR, installed the first railway semaphore signal at New Cross. The actual design is credited by Howard Turner in his three-volume LBSCR history to the engineer John Urpeth Raistrick. When the LBSCR was formed in 1846 by the amalgamation of the L&CR and the L&BR, the

Above:
Brighton North signalbox, built to John Saxby's design in 1862. The lamps were examples of Saxby and Greenwood's patent of 1854 (Nos 683 & 1830) the cases containing rotating coloured glasses for both directions. *The Railway Club/Pamlin Prints*

new company gradually standardised on the use of semaphores at stations and junctions, with the twin discs as auxiliary or distant signals to give advance warning to drivers of the former's indications. The faces of these discs seen by approaching drivers were painted red, with the backs coloured white with a black cross. The night-time indications of both semaphores and discs were made by separate lamps manufactured, from the middle of the 1850s, to an ingenious design patented by William Greenwood and John Saxby in 1854. The coloured glasses were fitted inside the lamp case and arranged so they could be revolved in front of the flame. With double-arm station semaphore signals only one lamp was used, with two sets of glasses to give indications in both directions, the rod for moving one set passing through the centre of the rod operating the other set.

In the 1850s the LBSCR installed a number of semaphores connected to a device designed by C. F. Whitworth which automatically replaced the signal to danger once a train had passed it. These 'disengagers' were fitted to the signals at Clayton Tunnel, and the failure of one of them was a contributory cause of the disastrous accident there in August 1861 when 23 were killed and 176 injured. The LBSCR soon abandoned their use.

Once the LBSCR had made a commitment to installing the absolute block system throughout its network in the late 1860s, mechanically operated semaphores became the standard outdoor equipment, the twin disc distant signals being replaced from at least 1872 by semaphores with a V-shaped notch cut out of the end of the arm. Photographs show that by the 1880s the arms of LBSCR semaphores were being made with a slight but noticeable taper from tip to pivot, the former a few inches broader than at the pivot. This simple design feature seemed to give the signals a particular elegance. Also discernible in early photographs is the distinct horn-shaped extension a few inches to the side of the pivot opposite the main arm. This was probably intended to act as the counter-balance to the main arm, a function superseded when the LBSCR redesigned its semaphores with a cast-iron spectacle attached directly to the arm which was pivoted on a casting attached to the left-hand side of the signal post as seen from the front. In this form, LBSCR signals were among the best proportioned of any railway company.

2. Signalling Equipment, Electrical

The first use by the LBSCR of the electric telegraph for regulating the movement of trains by signalman was at Clayton and Balcombe tunnels at the end of the 1840s. At those locations the signalmen at either end of the tunnel were instructed not to allow a train to follow another into the tunnel unless the previous one had been telegraphed out by his colleague. The equipment used would have been standard Cooke & Wheatstone 'speaking' telegraph instruments designed to give only transitory indications. There would have been no means of maintaining the current so that the needle stayed in one of its two positions.

Probably the first electrical instrument with needles capable of being pointed to and remaining in one of two positions was put into use by the company's Telegraph Superintendent, Mr Bartholomew, in the early 1850s. The instrument had two needles which could be pointed to either of the words 'clear' or 'closed', the right-hand needle for down trains, the left for up trains. The indications of each needle was altered by sliding a knob either to the right or left, this action bringing into operation an electro-magnet which also sounded a bell. As the action of moving the knob sent only a transitory current to the electro-magnet operating the needles at each signal station, they were weighted to maintain their positions once moved. The instrument was simple, but the indications were prone to alteration during thunderstorms, with the possibility that opposing indications were displayed at adjacent stations.

By the late 1870s, Bartholomew's instruments were no longer in use, replaced by those patented by Edward Tyer, founder of the most successful Victorian electrical signalling equipment business. Tyer had taken out his first patent in 1852 for instruments whose indications were changed automatically by passing trains striking a rail-mounted treadle. Both the LBSCR and SER experimented with the equipment, but from 1854 Tyer adapted the system so that the indications were under the control of the policemen and/or signalmen. Development continued over the next 10 years, and in 1862 he was granted a patent (No 3015) for a block instrument with four needles to control trains on double-track through lines. The needles could be made to point to two indications — Line Clear, or Train on Line. Two of the needles gave the indications sent by the operator, whilst the other two needles displayed the indications received from the adjacent signal station. The electro-magnets to change the indications of the needles were activated by pressing brass plungers on the front of the instrument case. Unlike Bartholomew's instrument, only one wire was needed to connect instruments at adjacent stations (with the usual earth return). A single-stroke bell (for signalling up trains) and a single-stroke gong (for signalling down trains) were also incorporated in the circuit, both sounding every time the plungers were pressed. Pressing down one of the appropriate plungers activated the circuit between the 'sending' and 'receiving' needles. The appropriate plunger rang either the bell or gong, and whilst it was depressed the current temporarily magnetised metal pieces around the appropriate needles on both the sending and receiving instruments. When the plunger was released, thereby stopping the flow of current, the metal pieces retained their magnetism, thus maintaining the needles at one of their two possible indications. By this simple means the deficiency of Bartholomew's weighted needles was overcome.

In the early 1860s the LBSCR, along with other railway companies, was being pressured by the Board of Trade to bring the block system into use on its lines, using instruments which could give permanent indications. Management resistance to making this considerable financial investment was weakened after the Clayton Tunnel accident in 1861, and when Tyer's 1862 instruments became available the LBSCR began to purchase and install them. Tyer continued to refine the electrical mechanisms particularly in the area of counteracting the effects of lightning, and in 1869 his patent No 2907 established the form of instrument which was manufactured in thousands for many railways in this country and abroad. Each instrument had two needles which meant that for controlling the passage of trains on ordinary double-track lines, two identical instruments were needed for each signalbox. It was this form of Tyer's instrument, modified with miniature semaphores in place of the needles, that became the LBSCR's standard block instrument. As with their outdoor equivalents, the arms of the miniature semaphores were slightly tapered and looked as though they were slotted into the miniature signal posts made from brass. When the arms were inclined downwards at 45° they indicated that the line was clear, and when horizontal that a train was in that section — Train on Line.

In this form Tyer's LBSCR instruments continued in use until the 1980s, long after all railway companies had adopted the Railway Clearing House standard signalling regulations of 1895 based around three indications — Line Clear, Train on Line and Line Blocked. In 1902 and 1919, Tyer & Co did patent two designs of one-wire needle instrument, both capable of displaying three indications, and just before the Grouping the LBSCR decided to install 1919 patent instruments on the main line between Balcombe and Brighton.

By then the company already had a semaphore instrument in use that could display three indications. Although very similar to Tyer's equipment, with bell and plungers, the instrument was manufactured to a design of Richard Harper, an electrical engineer from Finsbury. The miniature semaphores still only worked to two positions — as their outdoor equivalents — but incorporated into the instrument between the two plungers was a commutator which could be rotated to display Line Clear, Train on Line and 'Train off but section blocked'. The commutator had to be rotated to one of these three indications before the appropriate plunger could be pressed to alter the position of the semaphores. As with Tyer's instrument, the indications were altered by momentary currents and maintained by temporary magnets which meant only one line wire was required between instruments.

3. Signalling Equipment, Mechanical

Although at the time it was almost certainly not viewed as a landmark installation, in 1843/4 the

Above:
An LBSCR down train near Preston Park in the 1890s. All the visible signals were slot-in-the-post semaphores with Saxby & Greenwood lamps. The separation of the cast-iron brackets from the landing stage was a typical feature of Saxby & Farmer signals from the 1870s until the turn of the century, and this arrangement can be seen in photographs of other companies, for example, the GNR. *Locomotive Publishing Co/Bucknall Collection/Ian Allan Library*

L&CR brought into use the first mechanism for operating signals which incorporated some form of interlocking. At Bricklayers Arms Junction, where the L&CR left the London & Greenwich Railway (L&GR), Charles Gregory installed a modified stirrup frame for operating two points and four signals. The points were worked by levers independent of the stirrup frame and only the stirrups were arranged so that conflicting signals could not be given. The frame and the semaphores were built on to an elevated staging, and the whole arrangement impressed not only the Board of Trade inspectors but also the publishers of the *Illustrated London News*, who printed a view of the installation in their December 1844 issue. Brighton Junction (south of Norwood Junction) was so equipped in 1844, but once the L&CR became part of the LBSCR two years later, no similar work was carried out at junctions. The firm of Stevens & Sons began to manufacture and sell a number of these stirrup frames to other railways including the MS&LR and GNR.

The next development on the LBSCR did not occur until the company's carpenter and joiner, John Saxby, witnessed a train take the wrong route at Bricklayer's Arms Junction because, although the signals were interlocked with each other, the points were not. In 1856 he patented his 'simultaneous motion' frame of levers, so arranged that moving the levers operating the points also lowered the correct semaphore for the appropriate route. The equipment was first installed at Keymer Junction in the summer of 1856.

Saxby began to manufacture his new invention not only for use on the LBSCR but for other railways that wanted it. The simultaneous motion frame was not, however, despite the inventor's later

Above:
Sykes 'banner repeaters' used at Victoria (LBSCR) station, London, as platform starting signals. *Locomotive Publishing Collan Allan Library*

Above:
A close-up of the last form of LBSCR lower quadrant semaphore. This example was Hurst Green's up home. Of note is the company's preference for positioning the access ladder on the front of the post. This meant that as the lampman had to work over the top of the arm to get to the lamp case, he had to be careful not to be knocked in the chest if the signalman decided to pull off when he was in that position. *J. Scrace*

comments, the precursor of the type of lever frames that were eventually installed in their thousands all over the country. That was developed by Saxby and others after Austin Chambers of the North London Railway had in 1859 established a way of mechanically enforcing what became the fundamental principle of railway signalling, namely, that no signal could show all-clear until all conflicting signals were at danger and all points were set for the correct route (see p42). Saxby patented his first interlocking lever frame based on this principle in 1860 and it was immediately taken up by his employers. In October 1860, when the new Victoria station, London, was opened to passengers, it boasted a 23-lever Saxby frame — the famous 'Hole-in-the-Wall' installation — and the following year Brighton station was resignalled, with the new equipment installed in a number of elevated signalboxes.

The success of Saxby's equipment on the LBSCR encouraged the Board of Trade to put more pressure on other railway companies to install interlocking lever frames. In 1862 Saxby concluded an agreement with the LNWR to supply all its signalling equipment and this gave him the confidence to resign from the LBSCR and set up in business with John Stinson Farmer. Thereafter, his old company fulfilled almost all its signalling obligations by patronising the new firm, continuing to install the latest Saxby & Farmer equipment until the end of the century. The LBSCR did produce its own lever frame design in the 1880s based on Saxby & Farmer's Rocker & Gridiron pattern of 1874, but in 1905 it settled on a design surprisingly based on Stevens & Sons tappet frame.

In 1908 the company was more adventurous still when it brought into use an impressive installation of W. R. Sykes' electro-mechanical equipment at Victoria station and its approaches. The apparatus is described in the SECR section of this chapter. Six signalboxes were fitted out, the largest being Victoria South with 106 standard mechanical levers, for point operation, and 163 pull-out slides to control the signals, many of which were of Sykes 'banner' design.

Left:
LBSCR home and distant lower quadrant semaphores on the electrified south London suburban lines. When this photograph was taken before World War 1, both arms would have been painted red with a white stripe. To the right of the distant signal lamp is a Coligny-Welch indicator to help drivers distinguish distant signals at night. *Photomatic*

4. Signalbox Design

The earliest 'signalbox' (or, more accurately, signal tower) on the LBSCR system was erected by the L&CR at Corbett's Lane Junction where it joined the L&GR line into London. It was probably brought into use when the L&CR opened, in the summer of 1839, and was in effect a lighthouse, at the top of which gas lamps could project a red or white light, depending on the lie of the points at the junction. During the day a disc signal was used. Neither lights nor disc was used to stop trains or allow them to proceed, but simply to indicate which route was set. A similar lighthouse was built at London Bridge, but neither structure influenced the design of subsequent signalboxes.

The first stage in the evolution of signalboxes, as we would recognise them today, started with the erection of elevated platforms on to which double-arm semaphore signals and a signalman's hut were positioned. These appeared at junctions, the first recorded as having been erected in 1841 at Brighton Junction where the L&CR and the L&BR met. After this similar platforms began to appear at other junctions, and by the mid-1850s they were common.

The next evolutionary jump, when the signalbox really emerged, was also at an LBSCR location. Barely a year and a half after John Saxby had patented his 'simultaneous motion' lever frame, an elevated platform with the by then universal arrangement of two double-arm semaphore signals was erected at Norwood Junction in late summer 1857. But the platform differed in one very important respect from all those that had preceded it. In place of the small hut, the four posts supporting the platform were continued upwards to form the corner posts of a much larger glazed cabin with a hipped roof. In theory the walls were used to surround the platform, but the whole structure was obviously and visually a cabin on stilts, with semaphores protruding through the roof. A similar structure was put up that same year at Lewes Junction, and others quickly followed, so that by the end of 1862 there were at least 30 on the LBSCR.

From the middle of the 1860s, Saxby's signalboxes gained an additional room immediately beneath the cabin. This was achieved by simply boarding between the stilts and inserting a floor. Gradually, over the years, the room containing the levers and block instruments where the signalman worked became known as the operating room, and the separate room below housing the frame supports and often the locking was christened, appropriately, the locking room.

When Saxby left the LBSCR in 1862 his new firm continued to carry out signalling work for his old employees, resulting in the erection of Saxby & Farmer's standard signalbox designs. It was not until the 1880s that the company began to challenge this monopoly, in frame designs (as mentioned above) and signalbox architecture. The opportunity to influence the latter came with the building of a number of branch lines in Sussex between 1880 and 1883. The signalboxes still had much in common with current Saxby & Farmer designs, for example hipped roofs and small operating room windows, but extra details were added by the architect responsible for the station buildings. Beneath the roof there was prominent and deep eaves boarding and above the operating room windows there were cruciform ventilation holes.

This LBSCR Type 1 was confined to just three Sussex branch lines, but the design which followed found its way on to various parts of the system. These structures were either all-timber or had brick bases with timber superstructures. All had hipped roofs, and some had a decorative timber eaves awning to match that used on the station canopies. Operating room window sash units were mostly two panes high by three panes wide.

The Type 3, which superseded this design, started to appear in 1898. The new signalboxes had much in common with Saxby & Farmer Type 10 and 12 designs, and this may have been due to the appointment of W. C. Acfield as the railway company's Assistant Signal Superintendent in 1895, Acfield having previously worked as a draughtsman for Saxby & Farmer. The signalboxes all had gabled roofs, operating rooms clad in horizontal timber boarding, and bases either of the same material or of brick. Where the LBSCR structure differed most from the Saxby & Farmer designs was in the overhanging eaves at the gable ends and the panelled brickwork if the structures had masonry bases. The

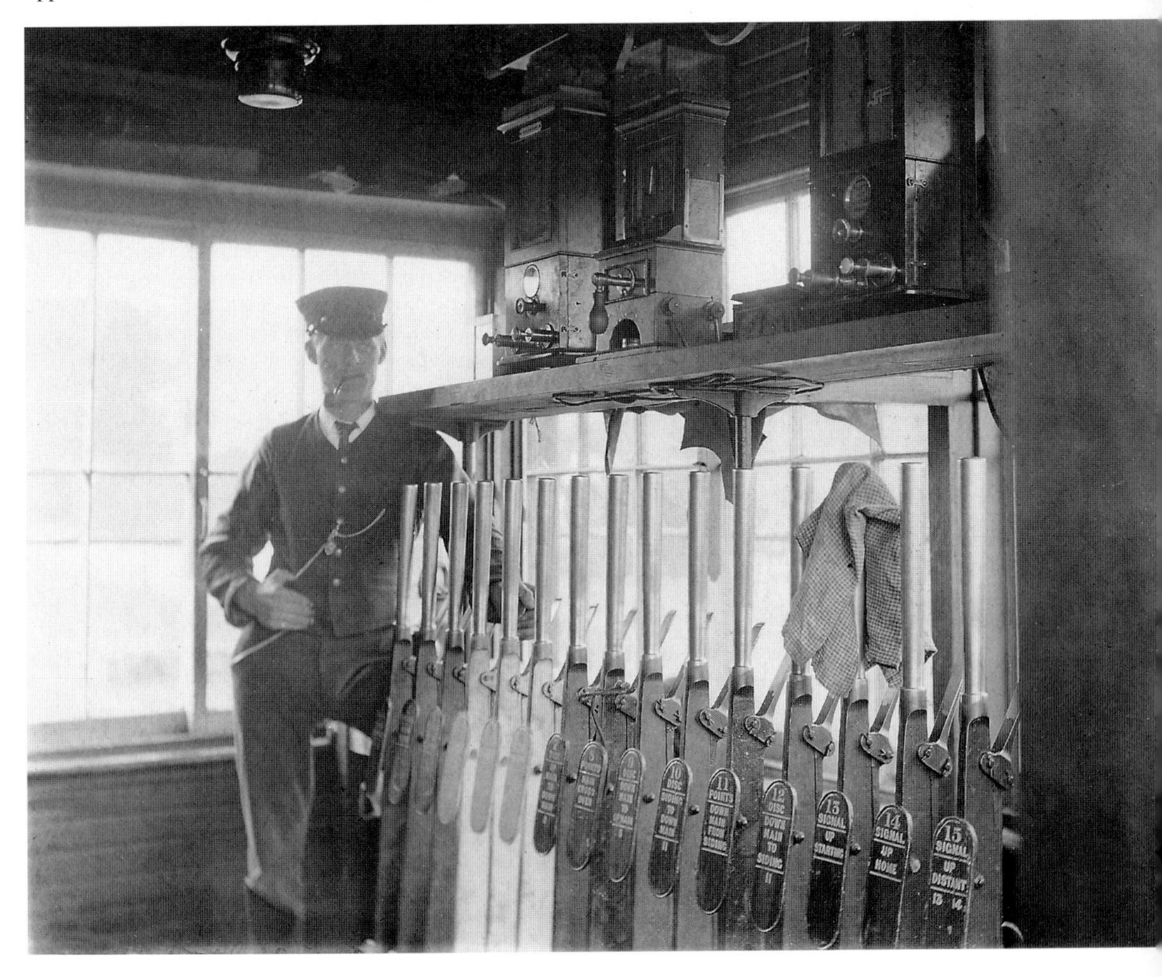

Below:
The interior of the LBSCR's Oxted Lime Sidings signalbox in the first decade of the 20th century. The leverframe is a Stevens tappet, and on the block shelf are two Harper's miniature semaphore block instruments with a standard single-needle telegraph instrument directly descended from Cooke & Wheatstone's electric telegraph of 1837.
Ian Allan Library

boxes built just before the end of the century had operating room window sash units of three panes high by three panes wide, whereas those built thereafter had larger glass panes, the sash units being only two panes wide by two panes high.

Above:
The standard LBSCR 1905 Pattern tappet frame installed in Clapham Junction 'B' signalbox, photographed shortly before it was taken out of use in 1952. *BR(SR) official photograph*

Above:
The LBSCR's Crowhurst Junction signalbox was one of Saxby & Farmer's well-proportioned Type 5 designs. *Ian Allan Library*

SOUTH EASTERN RAILWAY

1. Signals

The SER was an early user of semaphore signals manufactured from the 1840s by the firm of Stevens & Sons, Southwark, London. It is probably safe to say that by the beginning of the 1870s all SER stations were protected by 'station semaphores' with arms for controlling up and down trains pivoted in the same slot in a timber post. From photographs it appears that these semaphores were of a standard railway company design, somewhat different from Stevens & Sons' products. The most noticeable difference was the large lamp with an integral pointed finial which was mounted on top of the post. The lamp was of the same cross-sectional dimensions as the post, so that it appeared to be simply an extension of the latter. This configuration made these signals very distinctive. Two separate cast-iron spectacles with red (danger) and green (caution) glasses (both circular) were attached to the pivot spindles of each semaphore arm.

Photographs show that these signals lasted well into the 1880s, but by the end of this decade the SER, in line with other railways, was erecting separate signals for up and down lines at double-track stations. Many of these signals were derived from the existing 'station semaphore' design modified quite simply by removing one of the arms. As three-position signalling had been abandoned with the refinement of the block system by then and the 'caution' indication had become redundant, the slots in signal posts no longer had to be large enough to accommodate the semaphore arm for the 'all-clear' aspect. That indication was made with the arm inclined downwards at 45° — the former 'caution' aspect. At junctions, where the 'all-clear' aspect with the arm hidden in the post had not been used for many years (if at all), the slot in the post was already smaller than the 'station semaphore' variant, and consequently this design was adapted for signals on plain stretches of track. The lamps of these signals were not placed on top of the posts but usually a few feet below the arm, the post being capped by a wooden 'ball and spike' finial.

Sometime before the joint working arrangement with the London, Chatham & Dover Railway (LC&DR) came into force in 1899, the SER started to use a signal in which the semaphore arm was fitted into the cast-iron spectacle. Unlike the earlier spectacles the glasses in this new design were beehive-shaped. The spectacle was almost identical to that used by the LSWR and may have been a standard Stevens & Sons product.

2. Signalling Equipment, Electrical

As with all Victorian railway companies, the way the SER lines developed once they had been opened to traffic depended on the personalities of the management team and their overall vision for the company in response to both internal and external pressures. The SER was fortunate in employing Charles Vincent Walker (1812-82) as its first Telegraph Superintendent in October 1845. He was both innovative and responsive to the suggestions of the Railway Inspectorate of the Board of Trade, suggestions which began to take the form of 'Requirements' in succeeding years. Walker was the first to take William Cooke's theories of 1842 for controlling train movements by electric telegraph (detailed in his leaflet *Telegraphic Railways*) and turn them into a practical reality. By 1846 Walker had the electric telegraph in use over the whole of the SER, the first railway company to be so equipped, but in January 1852 he installed single-stroke bells at London Bridge station and Spa Road so that signalmen could exchange coded messages as to the running of trains. This simple system was progressively extended, so that by the beginning of the 1860s it was in use over 275 miles of track. No other railway had such a comprehensive system of train control. In 1854 Walker used Cooke & Wheatstone's double-needle electric telegraph instrument as a basis for the development of his own 'Semaphore Electric Telegraph' device, substituting two miniature semaphore arms for the needles. In this way he turned Cooke & Wheatstone's 'speaking' telegraph instrument, on which messages were spelt out by the movement of the needles alternatively to the right and left, into an instrument which instructed a signalman as to the position his outdoor semaphore should display. The wooden cases for these instruments were shaped like pointed arches and had other gothic details inherited from their larger and more ornate Cooke & Wheatstone speaking telegraph instrument predecessors. In the early 1860s, Walker's two devices were incorporated into the same instrument, the mechanism for operating the bell and the semaphores being patented in 1865 (No 488). By comparison, this instrument was very plain with no superficial mouldings at all on the wooden case. The new design became the SER's standard block instrument.

Unfortunately, one of the penalties of being a pioneer is that subsequent developments invariably render your own equipment redundant very quickly. Within 30 years the block system had evolved so as to make Walker's 'Semaphore Electric Telegraph' instrument outdated. The Railway Clearing House standard signalling regulations of 1895 were based on the 'closed' or 'affirmative' block system and this meant that block instruments needed to be capable

Above:
Grove Park, 1895, and a clear view of the SER's single-arm variant of its original slot-in-the-post lower quadrant semaphore design. In Time Interval working the twin glass spectacle would have had red (danger) and blue/green (caution) glasses, all-clear being displayed with the spectacle moved clear of the lamp to allow its whitish light to show. By the time this photograph was taken, the all-clear indication was displayed with the blue/green glass in front of the lamp. *Courtesy SECR Society via P. Coutanche*

of displaying three indications — Line Clear, Train on Line and Line Blocked. The SER management agreed to conform to the new standard but chose not to replace the existing instruments. Instead, the device for changing the indications of the semaphores was redesigned to incorporate a commutator and a mechanical trigger which could display a third indication — 'Train in Section'.

Walker also designed and patented (1874, No 1026) a pair of 'train describers' which were used to inform signalmen which route of a number of possible ones available an approaching train should take. The sending instrument resembled the wheel of a sailing ship, with a number of handles arranged around the circumference. Adjacent to these where enamelled descriptions of destinations arranged like the numerals on a clock face. By pulling the handle next to the required description and then pushing back into place the handle adjacent to the last description sent, a clockwork mechanism was triggered which rotated a wheel inside the instrument attached to a pointer on the face. The mechanism rotated until it was stopped at the handle just operated. A current passed to the receiving instrument at the adjoining signalbox, the instrument being identical except it lacked handles. The pointer on the receiving instrument was also rotated until it pointed to the required description.

3. Signalling Equipment, Mechanical

The SER was far in advance of other companies in electrical developments for the control of trains in the 1850s and for a time in the following decade it also had the most modern mechanical interlocking apparatus in the country. When the company opened its two new London termini, at Charing Cross and Cannon Street in 1864 and 1866 respectively, it brought into use two of the most impressive and influential lever frame installations anywhere. At Charing Cross the overhead signalbox with its Saxby 1860 patent frame and array of double-arm semaphores was built between the abutments of the River Thames bridge. The structure was not an afterthought but integral to both the architectural integrity of the station and, more significantly, its operation. At Cannon Street the overhead cabin was even larger and the same pattern Saxby frame there had 67 levers. The contemporary technical press was fascinated, but the General Manager was concerned that the complications of the apparatus would hinder the flow of traffic into and out of the station and threatened to have the locking between the levers disconnected if this happened. He was proved wrong and the installation undoubtedly helped the Board of Trade in its campaign to persuade all companies to use such equipment.

What is all the more interesting, considering the GM's views, is the completely different effect it had on the company's Engineer, Francis Brady, who only a year after the Cannon Street installation, patented a lever frame with his own design of interlocking (1867, No 1959). The locking mechanism was very compact and was positioned barely 2ft beneath and to the front of the levers. Access was gained by lifting up sections of operating room floor. Apart from the locking, the other main characteristic of Brady's frame was the very short travel of the levers (the distance the signalman had to pull the lever towards him), less than any other frame before or since. The frame and its interlocking also had the distinction of remaining in production longer than any other pattern which emerged in the 1860s. Examples were still being made at the end of the 1880s. In the following decade, tappet locking replaced Brady's own design, and production continued until the SECR standardised on a new frame patented by W. R. Sykes and E. R. F. Hallam (see page 112).

Brady's frames were not installed in every SER signalbox and in the 1860s Stevens & Sons supplied interlocking equipment. When Stevens started to manufacture frames with tappet locking patented in 1870 (No 746), the SER installed a number of those. Despite having been in the forefront of interlocking developments, surprisingly, of all the pre-Grouping companies which made up the SR, the SER was actually the last to have all its connections with passenger lines fully interlocked, not achieving this until 1895. Most of the work that had to be carried out to comply with the terms of the Regulation of Railways Act 1889 was done by contractors, and as a result Saxby & Farmer, McKenzie & Holland, The Railway Signal Co, Dutton & Co and Evans O'Donnell all supplied their own current lever frame designs and installed them in their standard signalboxes. At exactly the time when many other railway companies were actively trying to reduce the number of frame designs in use, standardising by either patronising just one signalling contractor, or manufacturing their own, the SER was increasing the variety on its network.

4. Signalbox Design

Of all Britain's railway companies, the evolution of the SER's in-house signalbox design is the easiest to trace. The block system based on Walker's single-stroke bells required the instruments to be under the supervision of signalmen, and photographs clearly show that by the end of the 1860s signalmen were provided with standard timber huts next to the station semaphores. These huts had horizontal weatherboarding with domestic-type casement windows and pitched slate roofs, a very traditional configuration echoing the functional designs of many SER station buildings. During the 1870s when larger structures were needed to house interlocking lever frames, the signal hut design was simply upgraded in ways that any jobbing builder would have understood. All-timber weatherboarded construction was retained, but, because the structure was no longer a hut but the next size up in terms of joinery, standard domestic sash windows were used instead of the smaller casements. The roof was also 'upgraded' from a simple gable pattern to a more architecturally appropriate hipped variety. These elements remained the hallmark of almost all SER-built signalboxes until the Grouping.

Using this basic design, and Brady's lever frame, the SER undertook most of its own signalling work in the 1870s and '80s. But, as mentioned earlier, the passing of the Regulation of Railways Act in 1889 highlighted how much work still needed to be done, and in order to finish in the time allowed by the Board of Trade, the SER was forced to employ many of the major signalling contractors.

LONDON, CHATHAM & DOVER RAILWAY

1. Signals

As with the SER, the LC&DR used semaphore signals from an early date. Until the 1880s the arms were pivoted in slots in the signal post, the company preferring metal lattice fabrications, with the spectacles mounted below the arm. The very distinctive 'elephant ear'-shaped spectacle castings with two asymmetrical oval glasses, a characteristic product of the signalling contractors Stevens & Sons, indicate that the LC&DR patronised that firm. By the end of the 19th century the spectacle casting and the arm had been brought together. What distinguished LC&DR signals from those used on other railways employing Stevens & Sons as the signalling contractor was the positioning of the arm on the post and the design of metal finial. Photographs show that the arm was invariably mounted very close to the top of the signal post and the finial was a simple flame shape, cruciform in cross-section.

2. Signalling Equipment, Electrical

The LC&DR's claim to fame as far as electrical signalling equipment is concerned was as the company where William Sykes perfected his electro-mechanical 'Lock & Block' system. Sykes was not the first to experiment in this area. C. E. Spagnoletti, W. E. Langdon and William Preece all devised ways of preventing a signalman from pulling his signals to all clear if the signalman to whom he was sending the train had not indicated that the line was clear. In 1874, in addition to the existing block instruments in Shepherds Lane, Brixton and Canterbury Road Junction signalboxes, Sykes installed unique equipment which was physically connected by rods to the station (home) signal levers in those signalboxes and electrically to each other.

The instrument took the form of an upright oblong box with two circular openings above each other, and Sykes secured a patent for this 'Lock & Block' equipment in 1875 (No 662). Clever though his system was, it had a fundamental flaw in that it could be operated without any trains being present at all! What Sykes subsequently added to the arrangement was a mechanical treadle attached to the rail and operated by passing trains. This was placed just beyond the home or starting signal (depending on which controlled entry to the block section). When that signal had been pulled to all-clear, the lever operating it remained locked until the last vehicle of the train had passed over the treadle

Above:
Folkestone Central signalbox was an example of the SER's in-house design of the 1870s. *R. K. Blencowe*

Above:
A standard Stevens & Sons signalbox design at the SER's Westerham station. *Author's collection*

which released the lever lock and allowed the signalman to put the signal back to danger. Once this was done, the lever was locked in that position too. The signalman knew whether the lever was locked or not by an indication displayed in Sykes' new instrument.

This new instrument incorporated a brass plunger. If the line was clear for a train to approach, the signalman pressed this plunger which then released the lever lock on either the home or starting semaphore of the signalbox from which the train was being sent ('in rear'). In Sykes' 1875 arrangement, this release had been achieved by the movement of the lever in the signalbox towards which the train was to travel ('in advance'). Pressing the plunger also (a) caused 'Train On' to be displayed in the lower aperture cut in the circular glass-covered face of the instrument, (b) caused a miniature semaphore set in a cylindrical glass-covered case immediately above the same instrument to change from the all-clear to the danger position, and (c) caused 'Clear' (or later 'Free') to appear in the upper aperture of a similar instrument in the signalbox from which the train was being sent. When the signalman at the signalbox which had obtained the release pulled the lever to clear his

Above:
A pair of lower quadrant semaphores designed for use in restricted spaces at the LC&DR's Herne Hill station. Mounting the lamps on top of the posts was a feature of early SER signals, but the shape of the spectacle glasses indicates these semaphores were definitely from the Stevens & Sons London works. *Locomotive Publishing Collan Allan Library*

home (or starting) signal, the upper aperture in the circular glass-covered face of his instrument displayed 'Locked'. When the train arrived and the signalman used the lever to put his semaphore to 'danger' behind it, the lower aperture in his instrument changed from 'Train On' to 'Train Passed', 'Clear' or just blank. Simultaneously the miniature semaphore arm was lowered in the instrument in the signalbox from which the train had been dispatched, indicating to the signalman there that the line was once again clear.

Sykes' redesigned equipment was patented in November 1880 (No 1907) and soon afterwards a 'switch hook' was added to the main instrument which was used to turn over the plunger. Turning the switch hook raised or lowered the miniature semaphore arm at the sending end. Other refinements of the 1880 patent followed, and the resultant equipment was installed on busy stretches of line mostly in the London area by all the companies which eventually made up the SR. Other users included the London, Tilbury & Southend Railway (LT&SR), G&SWR, Lancashire, Derbyshire & East Coast Railway (LD&ECR) and the Hull & Barnsley Railway (H&BR); the GER installed a particularly sophisticated version in 1896 on its London suburban lines.

3. Signalling Equipment, Mechanical

The LC&DR had 50% of all connections with passenger lines interlocked by 1875, compared to the SER with only 38%, and by the end of the 1870s the work was as good as complete. Stevens & Sons and Saxby & Farmer fulfilled most of the company's requirements using their own frame designs until the very end of the decade, when an in-house design became the preferred choice, even though contractors continued to be employed to undertake the LC&DR's signalling work. In the operating room the new frame looked very similar to that devised by Francis Brady for the SER, the levers having a very short travel. The framework supporting the levers was slightly deeper when compared to the SER design, but the locking was still located only a few inches beneath the floor, immediately in front of the levers. The LC&DR's frame was one of the first to use tappet locking after Stevens & Sons had let its patent lapse. It remained in production until about 1906, after which the SECR's New Pattern frame was used for new and replacement work.

4. Signalbox Design

In the majority of cases the LC&DR allowed signalling contractors to erect their own pattern of signalboxes. Stevens & Sons structures did not conform to any overall standard, but they did have a number of characteristic features. The end of every vertical board in the gable ends was chamfered or rounded on each corner, resulting in a saw-tooth pattern across the gable. The panes of glass in the operating room windows were also wider than they were tall, the reverse of preferred architectural convention at the time.

The Stevens & Sons style of signalbox influenced the LC&DR's own design, which was used on the Canterbury to Dover stretch of line in about 1878. These signalboxes, as with the signalling contractors' pattern, were functional timber structures with shallow gabled roofs. What differentiated them from the Stevens design were operating room windows with sash units either two or three panes high by three panes wide.

Saxby & Farmer erected a number of its different patterns of signalbox. Its earliest standard design built from the late 1860s into the early 1870s was an all-timber structure characterised by its shallow, hipped roof with almost no overhang. The small operating room windows, either two or three panes wide by two panes high, were positioned tight under the roof. By comparison, the next pattern to be used for LC&DR work was, in the author's opinion, the most handsome of all Saxby & Farmer's signalboxes — the Type 5, built between 1876 and 1898. Its hipped roof had generous overhangs on all elevations with decorative eaves brackets, and all the

Above:
LC&DR's co-acting home and distant lower quadrant semaphores at Sittingbourne station. Notice the metal disc positioned in front of the spectacles to obscure the green or yellow glass when the signals were in the 'on' (danger or caution) position.
Pamlin Prints

Above:
This photograph of the interior of the LSWR signalbox at Hounslow is included here to show Sykes 'Lock & Block' instruments. In this case, advance, starting and home signals on both up and down lines were protected with treadles. The Stevens tappet frame is also of interest as it incorporated two 'push-pull' levers (Nos 8 and 20). These saved space in the frame as from their normal position as shown, they could be pushed to work one piece of equipment and pulled to operate another. *BR(SR) official photograph*

top panes of glass in the operating room window sash units had rounded corners. The final two Saxby & Farmer designs used on the LC&DR both had roofs with simple gable ends and were christened by the Signalling Study Group as Type 10 and Type 12a.

SOUTH EASTERN & CHATHAM RAILWAY

In 1899 the SER and LC&DR were placed under the control of the South Eastern & Chatham Joint Committee. Various economies of operation were then possible including the amalgamation of the signalling departments. Naturally, old practices continued, and semaphores, lever frames and signalboxes of pre-1899 designs were still used for new work. A number of signalboxes did appear to a new design based on Saxby & Farmer's Type 5 but without the curved tops to the framing of the operating room window sash units. A new lever frame design was also introduced, having been patented in 1907 (No 27492) by E. R. F. Hallam, the Signal Superintendent, and W. R. Sykes Jnr.

The SECR's relationship with the Sykes company was of more historical importance, however, in the field of progressive signalling equipment. In 1901 W. R. Sykes Jnr had patented an electro-mechanical signalling system (No 7067). Traditional levers were retained to operate points, but above these were a row of pull-out slides to operate the signals electrically and built into the same fascia were the component parts of his father's patent 'Lock & Block' instruments. The aim was to reduce the size of signalboxes by concentrating the equipment into a smaller area and thereby increasing the efficiency of the signalmen. Sykes electro-mechanical equipment was installed in a number of signalboxes as part of the SECR's Grove Park widenings as well as at Folkestone. Interestingly, as mentioned elsewhere, a much larger installation of his apparatus was brought into use by the LBSCR in its half of Victoria station in 1908. The SECR did not resignal its side of that station until the very end of World War 1, and when it did it chose an American design of control frame (General Railway Signal Co, Rochester, New York), the pistol-grip pull-out slides working three-position upper quadrant semaphores.

Above:
The SECR's standard lower quadrant semaphore with twin glass spectacle and 'blinker' to prevent daylight passing through the blue/green glass and giving a false all-clear indication. This particular example photographed at Crowhurst Junction in April 1953 on its reinforced concrete post had a later enamelled steel arm. *R. E. Vincent*

SOUTHERN RAILWAY

In most spheres of railway operation, including signalling, the first decade of the 20th century was a period of innovation. The basic principles of block working and interlocking established in the 1870s had remained unchallenged for over 30 years, but at the very end of the Victorian era progressive engineers had started to take notice of developments overseas, and for signalling engineers North America proved worthy of attention. They were particularly interested in power signalling with pneumatic, electro-pneumatic or all-electric equipment, and three-position 'speed signalling'. As mentioned elsewhere in this book, a number of power signalling installations appeared in Britain before World War 1 brought further experiments to a premature halt. Although the theories of three-position signalling had been debated, little material progress had been made before the outbreak of war. It is clear that, had it not been for that conflict, much would have been achieved by using the American pattern three-position upper quadrant semaphore. These signals were motor-driven and were capable of displaying a red light when the arm was horizontal, a yellow light when the arm was inclined upwards at 45° and a green light with the arm pointing vertically. Separate distant signals were unnecessary as the new signal incorporated the indications of both stop and distant signals, and more importantly because the indication of each signal was dependent on the signal immediately ahead of it. The GWR had a single example in operation at Paddington in 1914 and the GCR installed others in 1916. Then a little more than a year after the armistice, the GNR had three in use at King's Cross, whilst the whole of the Ealing & Shepherd's Bush Railway and the SECR's half of Victoria station were so protected.

What prevented the widespread introduction of these semaphores, however, were rapid postwar improvements in colour-light signal technology, and by the Grouping of 1923 the ex-LSWR's Signal & Telegraph Engineer, W. J. Thorrowgood, was set to propel his new employers, the SR, into the forefront of signalling developments. In 1926, he and his colleague W. Challis completed a revolutionary resignalling scheme between Holborn Viaduct and Elephant & Castle which introduced a fourth aspect — a double yellow — to British signalling for the first time. Whilst other railways had only just started to move from two aspects — red and green — to three aspects by changing the caution indication on their distant signals from red to yellow, the SR was setting the four-aspect colour-light signalling standards which are still in force today. Cannon Street and Charing Cross were also resignalled on the same principle in 1926, and London Bridge station was similarly treated in 1928.

For these pioneering projects the SR used the multi-aspect form of colour-light signals as standard in comparison to the single lens, searchlight signals preferred by the LNER and GWR. The lamps and lens of the majority of the colour-light signals used by the SR were aligned vertically, but during the 1920s the railway company also installed what were called 'cluster' signals. The four lamps were arranged as a cross, with the yellow aspects top and bottom and the green and red lights either side. In the following decade this form of the colour-light signal was abandoned and the resignalling of the Brighton line and its South Coast terminal station in 1931/2 was achieved with vertically aligned multi-aspect colour-light signals.

For inter-war resignalling schemes the SR also embraced the miniature lever frame as supplied by Westinghouse Brake & Signal Co. That manufacturer had been producing such equipment since 1901, the main designer in Britain being W. A. Pearce. He had worked for W. R. Sykes and had been involved with power signalling projects for both the Westinghouse Brake Co and McKenzie, Holland & Westinghouse Power Signal Co in the years leading up to World War 1. In 1912 Pearce's Style 'K' frame went into production, and, as with all frames of the period, it was fitted with mechanical locking. Frames of this pattern were used in the SR's resignalling projects of 1926 and 1928, the new signalbox at London Bridge receiving a 311-miniature-lever example. This proved to be the limit of mechanical tappet interlocking, and the next Westinghouse development was a milestone in British signalling practice. The new Style 'L' miniature-lever frame had electrical (relay) interlocking, the most fundamental change in the way interlocking was achieved since John Saxby had developed his 'simultaneous motion' frame in 1856. The first Style 'L' was brought into use by the SR at North Kent East Junction in December 1929, and thereafter all future miniature-lever frames on the SR and BR(SR) were of this design. When Brighton station was resignalled in 1931/2 the new signalbox there was equipped with a 225-lever Style 'L' frame. Waterloo, Clapham Junction 'A', West London Junction and Woking were all resignalled in 1935 with colour-light signals and electrically operated points controlled from Westinghouse frames.

As well as the major projects mentioned above, the SR obviously had to maintain and periodically replace pre-Grouping equipment in a piecemeal fashion. All the pre-Grouping block instruments mentioned so far — Walker's double semaphore device, Tyer's and Harper's two-position miniature semaphore instruments, Sykes 'Lock & Block', Preece's one- and three-wire equipment — continued in use up to and beyond nationalisation in 1948, but the SR did attempt to standardise by designing and introducing a completely new three-position instrument. Worthy though the intention was, in practice all it did was add yet another device to the many others inherited by the railway company in 1923.

The decision to introduce the new instrument was made in January 1924 in response to the latest Railway Clearing House Rules & Regulations. Where Sykes 'Lock & Block' was still in operation it was agreed this should be maintained, but elsewhere the intention was to introduce the new instrument progressively. The design of the new instrument came about because Thorrowgood wanted to use 500 spare Sykes instrument cases, and convert others still in use when they were made redundant. The result was a particularly handsome instrument but one question which is still not adequately answered, however, is how many of the 500 spare cases, if any, were actually used. The glazed circular opening in the main wooden section of Sykes 'Lock & Block' instruments was larger than that used in the new design. As yet this author has not seen a standard SR instrument case which shows evidence of this opening having been modified. The majority of standard three-position instruments that survive were obviously not conversions but new pieces of equipment.

When it came to traditional mechanical signalbox equipment the SR standardised on the last Saxby & Farmer mechanical lever frame design. The frame had been patented in 1914 (No 4873) and manufacture continued when the firm became part of the new Westinghouse Brake & Saxby Signal Co Ltd in 1920. In 1924 the design was modified to become the Westinghouse A2 pattern, and in this form it was adopted by the SR as its standard mechanical lever frame in 1929. Its variant, the Westinghouse A3, was subsequently used by BR(SR) and continued to be installed into the 1960s.

Above:
The 107-miniature-lever Westinghouse Style 'K' frame photographed shortly after it had been brought into use in Charing Cross signalbox in 1926. The pair of circular instruments next to the block bell were examples of Walker's 'train describers', patented in 1874 (No 1026). The one on the right was for sending information, whilst the one on the left was for receiving it. *Modern Transport/Ian Allan Library*

As to signalboxes themselves, in the years immediately following the Grouping design broadly followed the last practice of the pre-Grouping constituent companies. Then in 1936 the SR introduced a very modern design that was subsequently christened the 'glasshouse' or 'Odeon-style' signalbox. These descriptions were a response to the large areas of plate glass and the rounded ends of the operating rooms, curves being a favoured feature used by contemporary cinema architects. Some of the larger structures also seemed particularly 'modern' because they were reminiscent of the latest ocean liners or battleships; the operating rooms, with their flat overhanging concrete roofs, were placed centrally on long brick bases incorporating not only the mechanical or relay interlocking but also accommodation for maintenance staff. On the smaller signalboxes the base was the same size as the operating room and was also finished with rounded corners. All these signalboxes had a broad concrete 'waist band' separating the two storeys, in the centre of which was the name cast in large upper-case concrete letters. Of all signalbox designs until then, this SR design best captured the more optimistic spirit of its age which was emerging after the Depression, the death of King George V and the abdication crisis.

Above:
Horsham signalbox, photographed shortly after it opened in April 1938, was a good example of the SR's most modern design. Classified by later signalling enthusiasts as SR Type 13, it is also known as the 'glasshouse' or 'Odeon' style. *SR official photograph*

Below:
Strood Junction signalbox was fitted with a Westinghouse A2 mechanical lever frame, and provided with the latest standard SR absolute block instruments for all lines except to and from Wickham Siding which continued to be controlled by Walker's double miniature semaphore block instrument. One of those large instruments can be seen at the right-hand end of the block shelf. *Real Photos/ Wethersett Collection/Ian Allan Library*

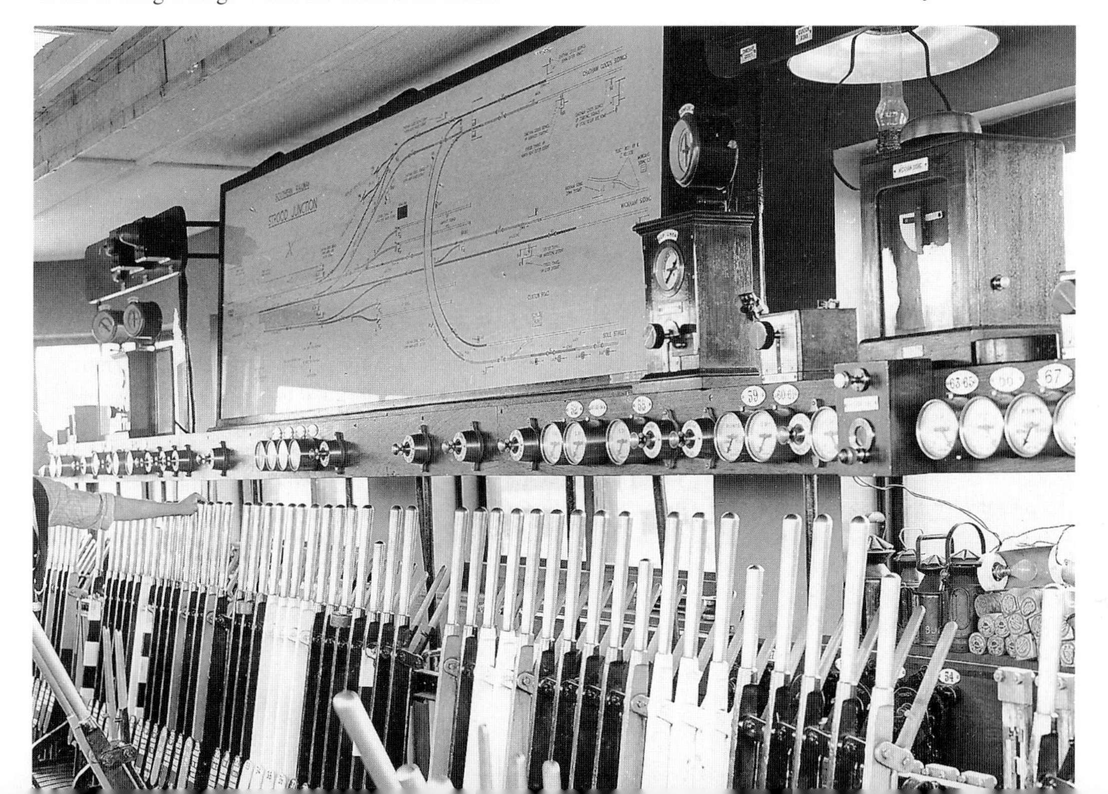

4
The Great Western Railway

The GWR can be viewed slightly differently from the other 'Big Four' companies created at the Grouping of 1923, because, compared to them, it was not really a product of amalgamation but more the result of the expansion of an existing organisation through the acquisition of a number of smaller railways. The pre-1923 GWR's corporate identity, created in large part by its standardised locomotives and signalling, continued until nationalisation in 1948 and beyond, and the absorbed companies were to a lesser or greater extent simply rebranded.

As there were no real rivalries to reconcile, existing practices continued and developed as though the Grouping had not happened. There was continuity. The 'greater' GWR continued to approach signalling in its own special way, the majority of its practices rooted very firmly in the late Victorian era. By nationalisation in 1948, the other 'Big Four' companies had taken some large progressive signalling steps — upper quadrant semaphores, four-aspect colour-light signalling, relay interlocking, route-setting panels, for example — all of which laid the foundations for subsequent BR developments. In comparison, after pioneering route-setting in the 1920s, the GWR had quickly succumbed to tradition, and when Paddington, Cardiff and Bristol were resignalled in the 1930s, although pull-out slides and miniature levers saved space in the new signalboxes, the signal engineers made sure that each slide or lever operated only one piece of equipment, just like every other mechanical installation. It is true the GWR installed new colour-light signals at all these places, but they conformed absolutely to existing standards, the indications no different from those of conventional semaphores. There was never any likelihood of the GWR adopting new-fangled four-aspect signalling.

Where colour-light signalling was too expensive to install, the other post-Grouping companies had agreed on a standard design of upper quadrant semaphore, but this was shunned completely by the GWR. A new signal with an enamelled steel arm and pressed steel spectacle was brought into use by the company only a few years after the Grouping, but this defiantly made its indications in the lower quadrant. This design remained in production until nationalisation, after which it became the standard signal on BR(WR) lines and many are still in use at the time of writing (2001). If Henry Ford had worked for the GWR he might well have said: 'You can have any signal you want as long as it is a lower quadrant.'

The one aspect of GWR signalling which did stand out as thoroughly modern, however, and which put the other companies to shame, was the widespread use of Automatic Train Control (ATC). In this area of signalling, continuity was a distinct advantage for the GWR, and after developing a workable system between 1905 and 1910, the company progressively equipped its main-line locomotives and track until by the end of the 1930s it had succeeded in fitting almost all its locomotive fleet and main lines with ATC apparatus. It was years before any other main line in the country was so protected.

Above:
0-4-2 No 556 was built at Wolverhampton in 1869 at a time when the disc & crossbar signal shown in the background of this photograph was being superseded by the ubiquitous slot-in-the-post lower quadrant semaphore signal. *Bucknall Collection/ Ian Allan Library*

GREAT WESTERN RAILWAY

1. Signals

By the time the first section of GWR opened in 1838, the practice of policemen giving three distinct hand signals to train drivers — Stop, Caution and All-clear — was already well established on the country's existing main-line railways. By then, fixed signals had also made their appearance, and the GWR soon began to erect its own. The very first was no more than a route indicator attached directly to a set of facing point blades at Maidenhead. When the points were set for the main line, a circular red disc with a white ring faced the driver, and when the point was set for the subsidiary route, the disc was turned through 90° so that it was edge-on.

In 1840 a temporary signal was erected at Reading which a driver had to be able to see before he could enter the station. This was contrary to the standard adopted on most other railways, where the only positive indications on fixed signals were for danger and/or caution, the line assumed to be all clear if no signal was visible. I. K. Brunel, who had already ignored 'narrow'-gauge track, was not about to adopt any other companies' standard signalling arrangement either, and when in 1841 he designed what has become one of the best known early railway signals — the 'disc & crossbar' signal — it was capable of displaying a very visible 'all-clear' indication. At the top of a very tall mast was mounted a circular disc, beneath which there was a rectangular board set at 90° to the disc. To reduce wind resistance, holes were cut out of the disc and slots out of the crossbar, but the most important feature of the design was that it gave both a positive danger and a positive all-clear indication. The former was indicated when the crossbar was face-on to an approaching train, and the latter when the disc was turned to face the driver. Originally the whole mast was turned through 90° by the policeman, but eventually the signal was redesigned so that the mast became a fixed post supporting a movable iron rod to work the disc and the crossbar.

To display a caution indication a completely separate signal had to be used. Originally these were the equivalent of hand-held flags but drawn across a metal frame like a curtain. They did not stand up to constant use and the British weather, and were soon replaced with a pointed board painted red on one face and green on the other. When the arrow head pointed to the track so that the red side faced oncoming drivers, this was the signal to stop. When the board was turned so that the green face showed and the arrow pointed away from the track, this indicated caution.

As on most early railways, the lamps used for signalling purposes at night were also viewed by the GWR as substitutes for the fixed signals used during the day simply because the latter could not be seen in darkness. Gradually companies began to link the

Right:
An example of the GWR's distinctive 'swallow-tail' distant signal arm. At some time this one had its cast spectacle removed so that it could act as the fixed distant at Donyatt Halt on the GWR's Creech Junction–Chard branch. *M. J. Fox*

Above:
Rear view of three of the GWR's first standard post-1893 twin glass spectacle semaphores at Grafton Junction in June 1951. Unlike a number of other companies' designs (eg MR, CLC, SECR, GER), the pivot of these semaphores did not pass through the post, but through a casting bolted to the side of it. The fabricated bracket shown here was also a standard pre-Grouping GWR pattern. *D. E. H. Box*

operation of the lamp with whatever signal they used, which meant that, although the lamp was lit only at night or during bad weather, the daytime signal had to be worked at night as well in order to change the indications of the lamp. In line with this new development, the GWR gradually attached its lamps to both the disc and crossbar and its board signals.

After about 10 years' service, the crossbars of the main signals were altered to help drivers identify from a greater distance which signal applied to them. Crossbars controlling trains travelling away from London were fitted with extensions below the crossbar at either end. Similarly, signals controlling up trains had extensions which were fitted above the crossbars.

The GWR remained faithful to Brunel's signals until the end of the 1860s, by which time standard three-position semaphores had not only been inherited with various 'narrow'-gauge railway companies absorbed by the GWR, but they had also begun to creep along the main 'broad'-gauge lines out of Paddington. As more and more signalboxes with interlocking lever frames were provided for the extension of block working, the 1870s witnessed the semaphore signal gradually outnumbering the disc & crossbar signals, the latter being replaced completely by the end of the century.

For many years GWR semaphores were very little different from those used on other railways. The arm was pivoted in a slot in the post, and photographs show that the single red glass spectacle was either fixed at the bottom of the slot or attached to the spindle of the arm. Contractors' designs were also used. From the mid-1870s, in line with Board of Trade Requirements, the GWR cut a section out of the end of its distant signal arms. Photographs indicate that on contractors' signals this was a simple V-shaped section, but on the GWR's own signals a very distinctive and pleasing 'swallow-tail' notch was formed. Although official documents record the GWR's decision not to erect any more slot-in-the-post signals after the GNR's Abbotts Ripton accident of 1876, photographs show that many remained in use until the very beginning of the new century. The same source of information also seems to indicate that the new design, with the semaphore arm pivoted on the front face of the signal post, almost invariably had the spectacle attached to the arm. This spectacle remained a single circular glass design until the Railway Clearing House standards of 1893 forced the GWR (and many other companies) to adopt green as the all-clear indication instead of white, after which the familiar twin glass spectacles began to appear. This spectacle was not redesigned until the mid-1920s, and hundreds remained in use well into the 1960s.

From this basic post-1893 design the GWR rapidly developed a range of standard arms of different lengths and shapes for special locations or for signalling specific moves such as calling on, or setting back. Rayner Wilson, Signal Superintendent of the L&Y, writing in 1904 described the GWR as 'one of the, if not the, most perfectly signalled railways in Great Britain . . .'. This was indeed a compliment from a man who boasted that his company had more signals per mile than any other. By then the GWR had also standardised on a particular design of cast-iron ball and spike finial with four varieties of slots to cap signal posts and dolls on brackets and gantries. These finials, like the arms, had a very long life, even longer if the modified version to fit later tubular steel posts is taken into account.

These posts first appeared c1925/6, slowly supplanting timber and reinforced concrete examples, the latter having been first used in 1917. Then in the first year of World War 2 the first bracket signals on larger diameter tubular posts were erected, followed a few years later by the introduction of a standard box truss fabrication made up of straight sections of riveted steel angle which was used in place of curved brackets. Once again these components remained standard on BR(WR) and gradually replaced many earlier castings and fabrications.

Above:
An interesting view at North Acton of standard post-1893 GWR lower quadrant semaphores on the right (the home signal yet to be brought into use), adjacent to what were in 1920, when the Ealing & Shepherd's Bush Railway opened, the very latest American-pattern electrically operated three-position upper quadrant signals. *J. Scott-Morgan collection/ R. S. Carpenter collection*

2. Signalling Equipment, Electrical

The GWR had the distinction of being the first railway company to use Cooke & Wheatstone's electric telegraph regularly to communicate between stations. Circuits were created between Paddington and Hanwell and between Hanwell and West Drayton and were brought into use in July 1839. Messages were exchanged by manipulating five centrally pivoted needles on instruments at each station. The needles were arranged in a line which formed the horizontal axis, or centreline, of a diamond-shaped grid of lines. Where the lines either intersected or joined, one letter of a 20-letter alphabet was placed. The deflections of two needles were needed to read off one letter. Words were then spelt out letter by letter. The diamond-shaped metal fascia supporting the needles and their electro-magnets was housed in a very elaborate wooden case, which in itself was a beautiful example of the cabinet maker's art.

This first installation had been comparatively expensive (each pair of needles in adjacent instruments being a separate circuit) and its benefits were not fully exploited by the GWR. When within a few years it needed attention, the system was not repaired. At the end of 1842 Cooke replaced the original system with a cheaper two-wire arrangement using twin-needle instruments, and this was extended to Slough in the following year. It was the use of this version of the electric telegraph to apprehend a murderer in December 1843, of course, which proved an invaluable publicity tool for Cooke.

The Paddington–Slough installation was used only to communicate general railway information, and the first use of the telegraph on the GWR to regulate the movement of trains directly came at the very end of 1847 when a circuit was established through Box Tunnel. The use of the telegraph in this way was gradually becoming standard practice on other railways and in the following decade it was used to control trains on single-track branch lines as well. Convincing railways to use the telegraph to implement the absolute block system on double-track main lines, separating trains travelling in the same direction by intervals of space rather than time, took longer, however. In 1849 the GWR actually ordered Cooke's Electric Telegraph Co to remove the Paddington–Slough installation, but this proved to be only a temporary setback, and beginning in 1852 the telegraph was not only renewed between those two stations but was also progressively extended on to Bristol. Five years later the company established its own telegraph department and appointed C. E. Spagnoletti as Departmental Superintendent — a character as important as Preece, Walker, Tyer and, a little later, Sykes, in the development of railway signalling in this country.

Left:
The impressive new gantry at Hatherley Junction, photographed in August 1944. The enamelled steel semaphore arms were attached to the GWR's final pattern of twin glass spectacle, whilst the tubular steel dolls were supported on the latest box truss fabrication spanning the tracks. *GWR official photograph/National Railway Museum*

Right:
A gantry of searchlight colour-light signals with their circular screens at Bristol in the early 1950s. The GWR arranged these exactly like traditional semaphore signals, so the stacked pair visible here was a stop signal over a distant. Between the tracks beneath them is the Automatic Train Control (ATC) ramp. *K. H. Leech*

The 1860s were a watershed between the old ways of the intuitive and empirical railway pioneers and the scientific and methodical ways of a new generation. Within this decade, almost all the basic electrical instruments which were to control Britain's railways for almost a hundred years were devised and patented. Preece, Walker and Tyer's inventions are dealt with elsewhere in this book, but here is the place to mention Spagnoletti's induced needle. Lost in his 1863 patent (No 2297) for a complete block instrument, and then refined in a later patent (1871, No 198), Spagnoletti's design of needle eventually found its way into thousands of instruments used by all this country's major railway companies at one time or the other. When the GWR began to install absolute block working from the end of the 1860s, the original patented form of his instrument was used with a card, or 'flag', lettered Train on Line and Line Clear attached to one end of the needle. The needle was placed behind a tin sheet with a small rectangular aperture through which the card could be seen. The whole instrument was far more compact than any then available, and instead of plungers or drop handles to change the direction of the current to alter the needle's indications, it used two tappers, or 'keys' — one red for Train on Line and one white for Line Clear — which could be held down by a steel peg attached to the instrument case by a length of brass chain. A non-pegging version of the instrument was soon brought into use, identical except that it lacked the tappers.

As with all instruments of this date, Spagnoletti's was designed to display only two indications, Line Clear being the normal position when no trains were passing between signalboxes. However, as the block system was refined in the 1870s and 1880s, the merits of a third indication — Line Blocked — became obvious. One of the reasons this indication was possible was because both Cooke & Wheatstone's and Spagnoletti's needles could assume a vertical position with the current switched off. Surprisingly, although the GWR adopted three-position signalling on its instruments, the card was not modified to display Line Blocked. What appeared in the aperture of the instrument when the current was disconnected and Line Blocked was signalled, was the join between the Line Clear and Train on Line lettering. This compromise is all the more difficult to understand as other GWR indicators using Spagnoletti's patent needle did have cards lettered with three positive indications.

Over the years the peg to hold down the keys was replaced by a loop made from a metal rod, the needle unit from the non-pegging instrument was fitted into an enlarged pegging instrument case, and two brass flaps were positioned over the keys. These were to be used by signalmen to reinforce in a physical way certain mental decisions they had made. The flap over the Line Clear key had 'Clearing Point Fouled' cast into it, and its use simply reminded the signalman he was not in a position to give a full Line Clear to his colleague. The other flap with 'Train at Signal' cast into it actually pushed the Train on Line key down so that indication was displayed on the instrument. A number of bad accidents in the first decade of the 20th century had caused all companies to re-examine their block controls, and these flaps were the GWR's response. They were progressively added to both original and 'combined' instruments, and then redesigned as a complete unit which was fitted as standard to all new instruments.

Spagnoletti's instruments remained the

company's standard equipment after 1923, and, even when new modular instruments were designed for the Bristol, Cardiff and Paddington resignalling projects of the 1930s, where they were fitted into the fascias above the pull-out slides or miniature levers, the familiar Line Clear/Train on Line flags were still used. The opportunity was taken in those new instruments, however, to replace the awkward twin keys and wire with a neat knob working a cylindrical commutator, but it was not until the very end of the GWR's independent existence that this formed the basis for a completely new stand-alone absolute block instrument. Spagnoletti's flag was finally replaced by a needle which could be pointed to three very visible and distinct indications. All that remained from the old instrument were the two flaps repositioned on either side of the commutator knob. These remained simple mechanical devices with no electrical link with the instrument at all. The very first set of new instruments were brought into use in October 1947, after which large numbers were made following nationalisation. As an interesting aside, the last paragraph of a BR circular distributed in 1950 to inform signalmen of the look and operation of the new instrument read: 'Manipulation. Very little force is required to turn the handle or to operate the reminder flaps. No good purpose is achieved by using undue force.'

In design terms the new instruments were a success, but as in many other instances before, the fact they were designed at all with so many other similar instruments in use throughout the country and available to the GWR just shows how inward-looking Britain's railway companies remained, and for how long.

To conclude this section of the chapter, mention should be made of the various power signalling installations of the GWR, both pre- and post-Grouping. Only a few years after perfecting its range of standard lower quadrant signals and fittings, and during the period when the final modifications were being made to the distinct GWR mechanical lever frame, the company experimented with an all-electric power signalling scheme at Didcot North Junction. The frame of miniature levers with all its associated control mechanisms was supplied by Siemens Bros & Co Ltd and commissioned in July 1905. The MR had also installed Siemens equipment in a signalbox just outside Derby only a few months before, but whereas that remained that company's only foray into power signalling, the GWR brought another two Siemens frames into use at an enlarged Birmingham Snow Hill in 1909 (North box) and 1913 (South box). The North signalbox was a busy place, with two signalmen required to control the layout with 224 miniature levers. As with the L&Y and LNWR power installations, block working was maintained with the companies' standard instruments and Tyer's train describers all fixed to a shelf above the levers.

Before the Grouping the GWR completed three further progressive resignalling schemes, the last propelling the company into the forefront of signalling developments. At Yarnton, just outside Oxford, and at Bath Road Junction, Slough, the latest all-electric apparatus supplied by McKenzie & Holland and Westinghouse Power Signalling Co was brought into use in 1909 and 1913 respectively. By contemporary power signalling standards there was nothing particularly novel about either installation. But what followed at Winchester Cheesehill, commissioned only months before the Grouping, was far more adventurous. The frame of miniature levers was based on the Siemens equipment mentioned above, but, instead of working individual pieces of equipment (or, depending on the position of the lever, two items) as with all previous frames, the levers worked only signals, the points moving as part of the 'route-setting' function triggered by the signals and track circuits. The frame and circuitry were patented (1918, No 125028) jointly by Siemens, L. de M. G. Ferreira (employed by Siemens) and R. J. S. Insell, Chief Assistant Signal Engineer of the GWR.

Put simply, a signalman pulled a signal lever controlling the route he wished the train to take to an intermediate position and, if the track circuits did not detect any trains in the way, the appropriate points were either held in, or moved to, the correct position for that route automatically. At the same time any conflicting routes were locked, and once this had been done the signal lever could be fully reversed in the frame to lower the semaphore to the clear position to allow the train forward. By pushing the miniature lever back to its second intermediate notch, the semaphore could be placed to danger, but the lever could not be fully replaced until the train had cleared the track circuit protecting the points. Until another route had to be set up, the points remained in whatever was their last position.

In the Winchester frame, lever No 9 was designated the King lever. Normally it was kept in an intermediate position in the frame, but when points had to be operated separately in cases of emergency, it was pulled to the reverse position, this action freeing slides located just below the levers which could then be used to work the points. When pushed to the normal position, the King lever could also be used to release the back-lock of a signal lever if it had failed to allow that lever to be replaced to normal in the frame.

The GWR was obviously satisfied with the Winchester experiment and in 1927/8 equipped two new and more important signalboxes at Newport station with the same route-setting apparatus. This was a bold step and far in advance of anything the SR or LNER had yet attempted. Then, for some reason, management abandoned further developments, allowing Tattersall at the LNER to carry forward the torch of modern signalling. When Paddington was resignalled in 1932/3 and Bristol in 1935, frames were supplied by the General Railway Signal Co with hundreds of pistol-grip pull-out slides each operating just one piece of equipment. At Cardiff, Westinghouse supplied two of its Style 'L' all-electric frames of miniature levers, Cardiff West signalbox which opened in January 1934 boasting the largest of these frames ever installed in this country or abroad, with no fewer than 339 levers, 229 of which operated two-aspect colour-light signals. Route-setting would undoubtedly have been of enormous benefit to the signalmen at these places.

Above:
The interior of the GWR signalbox at Hay-on-Wye with an impressive array of single line control equipment. Nearest the camera is a pair of Tyer's No 6 Electric Train Tablet instruments, then a pair of Occupation Control instruments, and at the far end of the box a pair of Tyer's Electric Train (key) Token instruments, classified No 9 by Tyer & Co. The latter had been developed and patented in 1912 (No 23417) by the GWR's Signal Engineer A. T. Blackall and his assistant C. M. Jacobs. *Author's collection*

3. Signalling Equipment, Mechanical

The GWR established a signal works at Reading in 1859, and the earliest date for the interlocking of points and signals on the GWR is stated as 1860, when equipment was installed at Paddington, Metropolitan Junction and Engine House Crossing. In the next few years, other places as diverse as Dorchester Junction and sleepy Much Wenlock received lever frames, many made to a pattern patented in 1865 (No 432) by the company's Engineer, Michael Lane.

By the end of the decade, a few key junctions were protected with interlocking lever frames, but not all were made to Lane's patent. When the Tenbury & Bewdley Railway opened in August 1864, for example, its junction with the GWR's Severn Valley branch at Bewdley was signalled by the signalling contractor McKenzie, Clunes & Holland (later McKenzie & Holland). The lever frame fitted into Bewdley signalbox was an example of 'Chambers Patent Junction Signal Apparatus' which had been patented in 1860, one of the first patents of this 'boom' decade of lever frame design. Chambers' design, like so many others, did not survive into the 1870s, but the employment of contractors did, and the GWR was not fully self-sufficient in the manufacture and installation of mechanical equipment until 1885. Saxby & Farmer and McKenzie & Holland received the lion's share of this work, providing their own lever frame and signalbox designs, but there were a number of locations where Gloucester Wagon Co equipment could be found.

Nevertheless, the GWR continued to increase its manufacturing capacity, and during the 1870s a new lever frame design was put into production at Reading. The locking in this new pattern was activated as the lever was pulled by the twist in a flat metal bar attached to each lever. This simple action sufficed until the 1890s after which the locking was improved by providing the bar with a twist at either end. The new design was christened the GWR Double Twist, and its predecessor not unnaturally became the GWR Single Twist.

Contemporary with the new design was the GWR Stud frame, which was made at Reading until about 1908. Both designs, however, had their disadvantages. Due to the way the locking in Stud frames worked, the maximum number of levers possible was 40, and in large Double Twist frames the travel of each lever had to be increased, which made them mechanically less efficient from the signalman's point of view. Nevertheless, these frames established the standard 'look' of all subsequent GWR designs: cast-iron quadrant plates with raised tread patterns fitted flush with the ribs which guided the lever in its travel, and a distinct pattern of catch-handle at the top of the lever and catch-box at quadrant plate level.

The next design, which appeared in December 1904, sensibly used the more flexible tappet locking, and when in 1908 the frame was modified by reducing the gap between levers from 5¼in to 4in, the standard was set for the final two variants which followed. The main feature which distinguished the first two patterns from the last pair was the orientation of the locking. In the initial design the trays containing the locks and tappets were horizontal. In the final variants the trays were fitted vertically, which made more efficient use of space in the locking rooms and eliminated the need for banks of trays in larger signalboxes. This final GWR Vertical Tappet five-bar design also displayed subtle differences in the lever travel and quadrant plate design, but overall it was unmistakably a product of the GWR's Reading Signal Works and was fitted into ex-GWR and BR(W) signalboxes until the 1960s.

4. Signalboxes

With little interlocking on the GWR until the late 1860s, simple huts must have provided the earliest shelter for policemen and signalmen. Once signalmen were entrusted with the operation of both block instruments and lever frames, more substantial buildings were erected, and in the 1870s both signalling contractors and the GWR's own design of signalboxes began to appear. A number of Saxby & Farmer's examples were built, almost all being of that firm's Type 2a pattern. McKenzie & Holland only ever provided three distinct signalbox designs of its own, all three of which were built at some time for the GWR.

The first in-house design, built from about 1869 until 1875, was an all-brick building with operating room windows set into the walls. Photographs show that signalboxes of this pattern were provided with either gabled or hipped roofs. These have subsequently been classified as GW Type 1. It is perhaps useful to remark at this point that the style of GWR signalboxes has been studied in great detail by members of the Signalling Record Society, and it is impossible here to do justice to the subtleties of their classification. Any reader particularly interested is referred firstly to *The Signal Box, A Pictorial History* (OPC, 1986, reprinted 1998), and then to the Society itself*.

Following the Type 1, and constructed until the beginning of the 1880s, was what we would now consider a more typical signalbox design, with continuous glazing in the front of the operating room. The majority of these buildings had wooden superstructures on brick bases and were given hipped roofs covered in slates. The operating room window sash units were almost always three panes high. During the 1880s the same basic design was perpetuated but with a gabled roof, and those signalboxes, provided in the northern areas of the GWR, where McKenzie & Holland had carried out much work, shared many characteristics with that contractor's design.

By the end of the 1880s the GWR was finally in a position to be able to build all its own signalboxes to a standard design. That design, classified Type 5 by Signalling Record Society members, was built in standard sizes with a gabled roof. The majority had brick bases which extended to the bottom of the operating room windows on the front and up to the eaves at the back. Window sash units three panes high were retained and many structures had an internal porch. Large numbers of these signalboxes were erected, especially after the 1889 Regulation of Railways Act, when the Board of Trade finally received the powers to enforce the completion of interlocking and block working on all the country's railways.

The signalbox design most associated with the GWR, however, first appeared in 1896 and has been classified as Type 7. It was the glazing of operating room window sash units which really created the design's unique identity. Each had five panes, three in the top section of the sash and two below. The proportions of these panes varied, but the bottom two panes were never less than half the overall height of the sash. Over the years other subtle changes were made to the design which have subsequently all been given their own classification type numbers, but the basic outline, cast-iron nameboards, sheet metal fabricated 'rocket' roof vents and characteristic window glazing remained unaltered. Examples continued to be built after the Grouping in brick, stone or timber, and a few were made up of concrete sections slotted into steel girder frames. Even when the GWR designed its own version of ARP signalbox during World War 2, with heavy brick walls and a flat concrete roof, the five-pane operating room windows were undeniable indicators of true GWR lineage.

On lines run jointly with other railways, the signalling equipment and signalboxes were often a mixture of GWR, contractors' and the other partners' designs. For example, on the GW&LNWJR John Saxby's influence was apparent in the style of signalboxes built along the Shrewsbury–Hereford line in the 1870s. The new signalboxes built in 1880 on another section of the joint line at Wellington

*The Signalling Record Society, c/o 51 Queensway, Wallasey, Wirral CH45 4PZ

Above:
Part of the GWR tappet frame in Oxford Station North signalbox photographed in February 1949. In the operating room the differences in the various tappet frame designs were very subtle and this one started life with either three-bar horizontal or vertical tappet trays. What is certain is that it was upgraded to a vertical tappet five-bar arrangement in 1942. *R. H. G. Simpson*

Above:
This Birmingham (Snow Hill) North signalbox may have been provided for the rebuilt station in 1871. What is certain is that it was replaced by one with a Siemens all electric frame of 224 miniature levers in 1909. *Author's collection*

Right:
Halesowen signalbox on the GWR's branch between Northfield Junction and Old Hill, photographed on 16 October 1966, was a McKenzie & Holland Type 3 structure. *Ian Allan Library*

station (Shropshire) were of that firm's standard brick design incorporating hipped roofs with prominent overhanging eaves and top-lights above the operating room windows. The design was obviously favoured by the Joint line's engineer, and when The Railway Signal Co won the contract to renew the signalling at Hereford in 1884, the box designs were almost identical to the Wellington examples. Shortly after this work was completed, signalling was put in the hands of the LNWR, and between 1885 and 1904 standard LNWR equipment was installed when renewals were necessary. After 1904 responsibility reverted to the GWR, and its standard signalbox designs and lever frames began to appear.

COSTITUENT COMPANIES' ABSORBED' PRIOR TO 1923

As with the GNR, the GWR either absorbed or took control of a number of smaller companies between the 1870s and the Grouping of 1923. Many of these companies when they were still independent had employed contractors to install interlocking and block working, and consequently the GWR inherited a variety of equipment. As it is impossible to give full details of all the companies in a book of this sort, the Bristol & Exeter Railway (B&ER) will have to suffice as just one example.

By the time this company had been absorbed by the GWR in 1876, all its lines were protected by the absolute block system using Edward Tyer's one-wire, two-position needle instruments and interlocking was as good as complete. Not surprisingly, considering Brunel's involvement with the company, the signals were of the disc & crossbar type. Signalboxes and locking frames had been supplied by Saxby & Farmer to its own patents, but the B&ER had also erected signalboxes of its own

Right:
Cookham signalbox was a well-maintained standard Type 5 GWR structure.
Ian Allan Library

Below right:
This particular standard GWR Type 7 signalbox at Bishop's Cleeve was somewhat unusual in being constructed with a stone locking room.
Mike Symonds, courtesy Stewart Blencowe

design. As with their neighbours on the GWR, and in common with the earliest types on the LSWR and the Southern Division of the NER, the signalboxes were solid masonry structures with the operating room windows set into the walls. Both brick and stone were used as building materials, and some signalboxes had decorative barge boards fitted to the gable ends. The known patterns used were unlike any used by other companies. Even the GNR, with its variety of barge boards, did not have comparable examples.

WELSH RAILWAYS

Grouping together all Welsh railways under one sub-heading when Scottish railways have been described separately may seem illogical and prejudiced, but the fact is there were far fewer signalboxes in Wales than there were companies north of the border. The Taff Vale Railway had the largest number — 118 at the Grouping. On that railway, interlocking was completed by 1881, an enviable record compared to other railways. Almost all of this work was carried out by McKenzie & Holland, which built a special variety of its standard Type 3 design of signalbox. Decorative barge boards, earthenware ridge tiles and finials gave these structures a very 'fussy' look. From about 1895 the design was simplified by fitting timber finials, removing the decorative ridge tiles and reducing the number of horizontal glazing bars in the operating room windows from two to one.

The type of semaphore adopted by the Taff Vale in the 1880s, along with the Rhymney and the Brecon & Merthyr railways, was the GNR style of somersault. Although the components, the spectacle and style of arm were all identical to the English pattern, the Taff Vale and Barry railways painted two white stripes on the front face of both stop and

Above:
Pontcynon Junction signalbox was an example of the Taff Vale Railway's simplified version of the specially decorated McKenzie & Holland Type 3 design used until about 1895. This photograph of 0-6-2 No 5691 passing the box was taken on 25 September 1964.
E. J. Ashworth

distant signal arms, each approximately 8in from either end of the arm. By 1910 both stripes on distant signal arms had been altered to white chevrons to echo the shape cut out of the left-hand end of the arm.

The earliest signalling on the Cambrian Railways was also carried out by McKenzie & Holland in the 1870s, but, when that firm began to supply somersault signals of GNR design to other Welsh companies, the Cambrian opted for its own unique design. This almost certainly first appeared in the 1890s, when the company was making a concerted effort to complete interlocking and block working on all its lines in order to conform to the requirements of the 1889 Regulation of Railways Act. This was yet another example of an independent company rejecting all the existing designs then available, to standardise on its own unique pattern.

When it came to signalboxes and mechanical lever frames, the Cambrian wisely allowed the contractors to use their existing designs. Dutton & Co and later Tyer & Co (after it had acquired the mechanical signalling works of Tweedy & Co of Carlisle in 1898) were both employed, although from 1901 Dutton's standard pattern was fitted into signalboxes irrespective of the contractor. By the Grouping, the Cambrian calculated it had 92 signalboxes.

The only Welsh railway company not to use McKenzie & Holland for the majority of its signalboxes and interlocking was the Barry Railway, which employed Saxby & Farmer and Evans O'Donnell.

Above:
This is not the best of photographs, but it does show an enamelled steel GNR-style somersault arm with two white stripes still in use on the former Barry Railway at Southerndown Road station in August 1961. The lower of the two landing stages and the patch left on the signal post indicate that originally the spectacle and lamp were positioned a few feet below the arm. *Rev R. P. Griffiths*

Above:
The Cambrian Railways' own design of lower quadrant semaphore photographed at Fairbourne in July 1962. *J. Scrace*

Left:
The Cambrian Railways' signalbox at Pwllheli West had been provided by Dutton & Co to its standard Type 2 design. Not surprisingly, considering that the firm's founder, Samuel T. Dutton, had previously worked for McKenzie & Holland, the design had many similarities with that firm's signalboxes (eg the semi-circular heads of the locking room windows). *G. S. Cocks*